finding Spirit
in
Zen Shiatsu

Finding Spirit in Zen Shiatsu

Design Uta Demontis
Photography Kris Deva North, Gudrun Mohrmann,
Keith Saunders
Zen Art Kris Deva North
5-Element Cycles Sutharshini
Research Jaclyn Snyders

Grateful acknowledgement is made to the following for
permission to reprint previously published material by
Kris Deva North: Positive Health Magazine: excerpts
from 'Calabash of Light' and 'Shiatsu: Ancient
Techniques for the 21st Century'; Qi Magazine: 'Zen as
a Philosophical Discipline.' Mantak Chia: 'A Touch of
Sex, Shiatsu Secrets for Love.'

First published 2006 by
Universal Tao Publications UK
1st Floor, 68 Great Eastern Street
London, England EC2A 3JT
Tel: +44 (0) 207 739 9916
email: info@healing-tao.co.uk
web site: www.healing-tao.co.uk

ISBN: 0-9554430-0-8
ISBN: 978-0-9554430-0-8

Printed in England by
Premier One Solution

To the students, practitioners and teachers of Zen Shiatsu, in all its forms and none.

With gratitude to the many who tried to show me their Way, and thanks to those who helped me find my own.

"Treat my words like Gold: Test them for their Value, their worth to you."

True Spirit of Zen
Dwells closer within
Than breath in my Lungs
Still closer to me
Than blood in my Heart

Contents

Preface   9

Chapter 1: Travelling Light   11

Chapter 2: Death and Birth   29

Chapter 3: Working Zen   43

Chapter 4: Learning by Heart   57

Chapter 5: Leaning with Love   83

Chapter 6: Spirits of the Being   117

Chapter 7: Hara Shiatsu   133

Chapter 8: How to make your living doing what you love   141

Chapter 9: Case Studies in the Spirit of Zen Shiatsu   157

Chapter 10: Coping with Assessment   171

Training Information   177

Contact Information   179

Glossary   181

Bibliography   183

Author   185

Preface

When I first began teaching Zen Shiatsu I tacked signs to palm trees on the dusty path from the boat-landing to catch the eyes of new arrivals on the hippy island of Koh Pha Ngan. The notices invited people to meet me at the Coconut Theatre on Leela Beach, to learn the Art of Gentle Healing. I asked them to bring an open mind and something to lie on.

Now I hang my notices on Google and provide the something to lie on: comfortable futons in a beautiful room in the City of London, at the Zen School of Shiatsu. But I still ask you to bring an open mind.

Learning shiatsu has changed my life. Like you, like everyone, there were always things I wanted to change. Stuck in the mundane dimension (spirit-speak for rat-race), earning my living in the hustler world of commercial property, I could afford neither to stop what I was doing nor start something new. Then, in the tradition of Zen good-luck/bad-luck stories, something happened in my personal life. About the time I was beginning to realise I could look at such events in a different light, my friend Patricia sent me a newspaper clipping about shiatsu training. Next day I signed up.

In learning to heal others I learned to heal myself.
In learning to teach others I learned to teach myself.
I learned that every experience is a learning-experience and that sharing makes me feel good.

That's why I've written this book, about finding Spirit in Zen Shiatsu. There have been plenty written about techniques and suchlike. These are listed at the back. In this, I want to share my spirit, the spirit I found in this wonderful work of helping people learn to help others.

I thank Sheralee, co-founder of the Zen School, who helped me through the first years with every kind of support. You would be proud of what we started, Lee: come back soon.

I thank my co-teachers Michael, Liz, Megan, Bernadette, Doug, Alex and Sue, for their contributions over the years, for sharing their ideas, for making me explain mine, for supporting or challenging in all the right places. It is they who give the Zen School its 'Spirit of Place.'

I thank our students who are really our teachers. I've learnt more from teaching than I ever did studying. And special thanks to Uta for her design and layout, and Jaclyn for her research.

I thank those who inspired the stories: if you only knew how you have helped; and I thank Richard Bandler, Paul McKenna and John La Valle for teaching me how to tell those stories.

I thank my early shiatsu teachers, Saul Goodman, Liz Arundel, Hilary Totah and Neil Gulliver; Nigel Dawes who inspired me to continue learning and encouraged me to go to Master Suzuki in Japan. Thanks too, alphabetically, to the great and the good from the other shiatsu world who have visited our Zen School and shared their teachings: Veet Allen, Thea Bailey, Carola Beresford-Cooke, Simon Fall, Sue Hix, Nicola Pooley, Michael Rose, John Tindall, Suzanne Yates. I thank the Taoist Master, Mantak Chia, for all he has taught me of the deep healing practices that underpin our "finger-push." And thanks to the Rainbow Family of Living Light for saying "We love you."

I apologise to anyone I have forgotten to mention, with thanks for whatever you did to help and or inspire.

And I thank you, for reading my book. If you like it, share with a friend. If you don't, tell me! Feedback helps, always and in every-thing.

Kris Deva North   London 2006

Chapter 1
Travelling Light

Travelling Light

Spirit jumps out from unlikely places and slaps me. I am buying a pair of trainers in Varanasi, shopping in a widow-lined alley near the burning ghats. A faint barbecue smell wafts by. The keen young man in fawn trousers and bright blue blazer shoves away the cow blocking his shop door and lets me in. He can offer me only one pair, brown, in one style, in a size quite close to mine. I try them on between sips from a tiny cup of sweet milky tea. He asks, "What is England like?" Educated at an English-medium school he has not seen that land which left him its language and a love of cricket.

What's England like? What words could describe the differences between our countries? "Less crowded. Bigger buildings. We abandon our elderly to care-homes rather than the street. And more choice. There you could go into a shoe shop and choose from ten colours in twenty styles and all sizes." His eyes widened.

I said, "What's India like?"

"India is a place where minds can meet."

Elsewhere spirit kept a lower profile. When I began shiatsu I was told to buy a book listing symptoms and related meridians. The Way of Memory led to a written examination and a headfull of information to carry around the world. My plan was to learn more, by meeting remarkable men and women. Five years wheeling and dealing in London property had awarded me time to go in search of the miraculous, resolve my mid-life crisis, maybe clean a little karma, and remove a few stones from the calabash.

Where to seek the wise ones? Nowadays the click of a mouse pops up a dozen for less than a dime as engines do the searching. Christ on Google would have had the pick of twelve just men from among two hundred and seventy-four million pages of them. Then? Those few shiatsu teachers who had trained in Japan seemed to have something extra, something special. I could not for the life of me work out what it was but, whatever it was, I wanted some. Checking out the cost of a return flight I found that an extra fifty quid would take me all the way round the world to complete the fulfilment of childhood dreams, trek the Himalayas, walk the Grand Canyon, see the Declaration of Independence – drafted by, among others, Tom Paine, from my parents' village in Norfolk – and new dreams of finding spirit.

One of those travellers who absorbs the guidebook before getting on the plane, I would arrive somewhere, eyes riveted to map. A man sitting on the steps of the Jade Buddha temple in Chiang Mai said to me, "Throw it away!"

"What?"

"The map, the guide-book."

"But how will I know where to go?"

He shrugged. "Jump off the cliff. More fun to get lost. The universe, she always smiles when you trust her."

I changed the practice of a life-time and wandered about, asking my way (or noticing I was too scared to do so.) I saw, heard and felt many things I would have missed, and admittedly did miss a few standard tourist sights, looking at maps or guidebooks after I had left somewhere. But how exciting! It was interesting on those far journeys to read advice to avoid an area, for whatever reason, after I had spent time there in blissful ignorance. I really got the feeling of the journey, of the moment of now, rather than looking ahead to the future and letting the present slip by unnoticed.

Discouragement sprang sly ambushes: the airport in Tokyo with not a word written in English and every person I approached – however hesitantly – scurrying away as if in fright. The universe smiled in the form of a kindly man wearing the blue badge denoting he was someone who had undertaken to be nice to foreigners. He showed me how to put money in the Japanese-speaking ticket-machines.

I had made friends on the way who assured me of a place to stay in their expensive city. I called from the airport. Hatsumi was still in India. Nobuka's voice said "Welcome to Japan" before telling me I could not stay there as her brother was away and the family thought it inappropriate for a man to stay with her alone.

A small box ad in the Japan Times pointed me to small box accommodation in a gai-jin house. Gai-jin means foreign devil. 45,000 yen, in 1992 about £200, bought me a month on a top bunk with sheets that needed a wash, in a 4 paces x 3 room without curtains, shared with five Iranian illegals who started their days at the labour-market in Ueno Park, worked shifts in a chemical plant and came in at all hours smelling of old eggs and turning on the television: Sesame Street, electric-cage wrestling, real-death pictures of suicide jumping, close-ups of car-crash victims, hot-air balloons on fire incinerating the occupants.

On the dangerous half-hour walk to the Subway I was narrowly missed by speeding pavement cyclists; passed vending machines of snacks, drinks, cigarettes, tins of cold beer, hot tea, coffee, chocolate, plastic glasses of sake. Pedestrians waiting long minutes on an empty road frowned at me crossing before the light turned green.

Rush hour cracks the mask of traditional courtesy: crowds fighting with body-weight and surreptitious elbow-strikes to get through the subway turnstiles then stand, polite again, in regimental rows on the white lines marking where the train doors will open. Strong men in uniforms with peaked caps and white gloves pack passengers into clean crowded coaches. People talk to each other on the Tube – a novel concept for me, a Londoner. It was an hour to downtown. A million people an hour pass through Shinjuku station.

Ginza: a combination of Oxford Street on speed and Soho after dark. I had a feeling that if I closed my eyes and woke up in Thailand or Nepal I would burst into tears of relief. It was just so crowded, unfamiliar, full on. I felt as I had in London before building the support systems of friends, chi kung in the park, working in the rehab clinic, visiting shiatsu clients, going to practice-classes.

I paid 200 yen to enter a pretty park. People strolled around enjoying cherry-blossom time, battalions of salary-men and women, neatly dressed, walking through orderly trees on lawns so perfect they looked artificial. A group stood in tense silence, watching a man prune a tree. I felt quite excited myself. Surprising numbers of tramps and bag ladies loitered, even around the temples: a few dossers had their heads down at the great Kannon shrine.

I called the Iokai, the late Masunaga's clinic. Speaking English, a man said he did not run classes and no, I would not be permitted to observe or assist at any treatments. "Suzuki has a good clinic," he said.

That's where I was heading anyway.

Takeo Suzuki, thickset in white gi, black hair side-parted, beetling brows, told me to put away my notebook.

"Shiatsu must be learned with the body."

He watched me work for a few minutes.

"You do it like a mechanic. Mechanical manipulations. You take both hands off and lose connection. When you lose connection with the body, you lose connection with the ki and you lose connection with Spirit. You get into rhythm and lose sensitivity."

I glared at the interpreter. "I did some training in London with the legendary Shizuto Yamamoto. She told me it takes five hundred treatments to develop sensitivity. I still have over a hundred to go."

Suzuki disagreed. "One moment of awareness is worth a hundred hours of practice. In shiatsu, awareness is sensitivity: let it develop from the start. Empty your mind of all that learning; focus on how your patient responds to every touch. Go in slowly, sense the essence, come out as slowly.

"Think like a samurai, touch like a mother."

The veil lifted. Memorising symptoms and pushing points were of the world; seeing into the essence a step into spirit.

"The Zen mind, enlightened and disciplined, is able to rise above mere technique and go straight to the core of being...to reach the soul...the essence."

RYUKYU SAITO

The universal smile widened in the honeymoon isles of Hawaii:

"Our culture began to die," said the Kahuna, "when a people arrived in our islands who preached a doctrine of Love but practised the doctrine of material Possession. Our dancing and singing were forbidden by their missionaries, whose children took over the land for commerce and whose families still own it. They brought diseases unknown to our immune system. In 200 years our population fell from 400,000 to 150,000.

"They banned our medicine as superstition: if a sickness prevails, the Kahuna finds out from Spirit what healing the soul needs for the body to be whole again. We know that everything is a gift and a blessing, for everything is Love, and gratitude and thanks must be given even for hurt and pain. Then harmony can be restored between soul and body.

"Each child is born of the Rainbow and there at death returns. We are born perfect and gifted by the gods with a calabash of light to illuminate our way. In our passage through this life each sadness, hurt or wound given or received adds a pebble to the calabash, obscuring the light. Each joy removes a pebble, increasing our radiance. When our time comes to step back upon the Rainbow, the more light radiating from our calabash the sooner we find our way home.

"Our thoughts are our reality and we can change both. We embody every thought we have had, every thought another has had about us. We are the good we have done and the bad we have done, the good that has been done us and the bad done to us. The good and the bad of the past have become our thoughts. The good and bad of the present depend on how we react to events in the present. We can change the karma brought from before by our thoughts, and we can change the effect of what happens now, by our responses. We can take pebbles out, or put more in. We can face the sun and let the shadows fall behind. Or we can choose to be in the dark.

"Most of you" he smiled, "live in twilight, with occasional patches of brilliance or shadow. Each thought is a choice."

I had begun the Way of Understanding which over the years evolved into a true Zen approach to shiatsu, the ethos of the Zen School, the open secret: that all you need is Love, to open your heart and let the love flow, unconditional, giving without demanding a receipt, and receiving without transaction, a formula for true love, in all its ways - compassion and passion, adoration and lust, delight and desire, ecstasy and pleasure and as many more as you have known or can think of.

You can find yourself in love as easily as lose yourself in love. The safety is in the surrender, rather than hiding. Surrender to what? To others' ideas of what should be, what you should be? No. Surrender to yourself, to your inner nature, your truth, your beauty. Your Self.

Do you need to give? Then give. You don't have to wait for a receiver who can accept all you have to give. Just give. With all your heart, or as much of it as you want.

Do you need to receive? Then receive. You don't have to wait for a giver who measures out your precise dosage: receive what is given, let the excess overflow and cry not if it's too little.

Be yourself, and live and die, being yourself '...and all the rumours of the hard and cold let us now value at a pennysworth. Suns when they set can rise again; for us, when once our brief light has expired, then comes the night....'

Yin flows into and becomes Yang, Yang becomes Yin: day and night, warm sunshine and cool shadow: Absorb the sun, rest in the shade. We are born yang, with noise and movement; we die yin, into peace and stillness.

"As sure as death for the born, so sure is birth for the dead. Like joy, like grief, all things shall pass."

BHAGAVAD GITA

Yang rises and falls, as does Yin in harmony. It is how you see it – harmony or opposition. Your heart stops with every beat, so it may beat again; your lung stops with every breath, so it may breathe again. In the spaces between the beats and the breaths, life happens: only the void is constant, the empty force, the greatest in the universe, what Albert Einstein called, Love.

Can you understand the fears arising from experience which you can leave behind you in the past – its over – while you go on in freedom, to be yourself, as you are, in all your shining beauty? I heard a man shout on a mountain in Colorado, "Be Yourself!"

He held the Talking Stick: we could neither speak nor eat till he had done. He roamed around the campfires, a little man in orange shorts and wild Indian hair, shaking his thin arms and shouting, Be Yourself, nothing but that. Earlier that day I sat at the edge of the pine forest, looking down a great green valley, at thousands of rainbow-drops walking through swaying grass beside a crystal lake, under a backdrop of snow-capped peaks. They streamed up the valley, wanderers, traders, musicians, men, boys, women, kids, dressed in all the colours, some in rags, some in leathers, tribal families hung about with beads and feathers, Hindu saddhus, Buddhist monks, cowboys alongside Flower Children. It was the annual gathering of hippies, the Rainbow Family of Living Light and I had hitched from Los Angeles to join them. Each new arrival was greeted with a hug and "Welcome home, we love you." I felt stiff and British.

Tented camps known as kitchens spotted the slopes, each manned by volunteers serving a few hundred people. Everything was free: as much food and tea as you could eat and drink. I had no tent, not even a sleeping-bag so I slept in the sunshine by day and at night when the temperature plummeted below freezing, sat around camp-fires swapping tales with world travellers and listening to blue-grass music or stood in line at TeaTime meeting people and ideas that caused an avalanche in my mind.

I joined the multicoloured human stream flowing up to Main Circle, all in silence. At noon on July 4th a great shout rose and spread among the thousands filling the grassy floor of the valley and up through the thousands sitting on the slopes, and down the path of the hundreds still arriving, a great shout that turned into a cheer and then a John Lennon song: Imagine. The drums began, atavistic rhythms I had first heard in Africa. I pressed forward into the crowd.

A wooden post about eight feet tall and decorated with coloured cloths, feathers and bones stood at the centre, some twenty drummers making a passageway for the dancers, naked, body-painted, some in flowerpower clothes. Soon everyone was dancing, the whole crowd, through the afternoon, into the evening, high on acid, marijuana and love. A couple made love surrounded by cheering clapping dancers.

On the fringe of the throng I heard an argument between one group who wanted another to burn the American flag they were carrying: it was supposed to represent 'one nation' which the protesters said the United Sates certainly was not. And for every ten who cried 'Peace, brothers and sisters' there were two or three to shout 'No peace before justice!'

They were strong but peaceable in their beliefs and sincere, and angry at what their government was doing to the environment. A Hopi chief came to the circle to ask for witnesses to his village's impending forcible eviction from Big Mountain, which had been leased, to a mining company. I later heard the eviction had not happened: the presence of a large group of white, articulate witnesses.

I was surprised to be addressed as 'brother' but got over my self-consciousness by remembering the priests and monks and nuns at boarding schools who had to be called brother, sister, mother, father regardless of their brutality. Now I could say brother to men who feel like brothers to me, who smile and talk and are interested in more than themselves.

The talking circle was held each evening before dinner. We stood holding hands in a circle that encompassed the floor and slopes of the valley up to the edge of the pinewoods and twenty thousand voices sang a long deep high Om. Then every other person took twenty paces forward to make an inner circle. Then from each of those two circles, every other person took ten paces forward, making two more circles. Those in the inmost circle turned outward to face those in the second, while those in the third turned to face those in the outer circle. Thus we had four concentric circles making two round corridors around which the volunteers from the kitchens dragged containers of food and ladled it out. And all this was achieved with precision and without fuss or shouting.

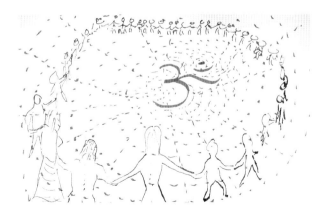

A band of musicians danced and sang around each circle carrying the Magic Hat. I put in a five-dollar note. My neighbour, a tall ginger man from the Elvis Lives kitchen, wearing nothing but a black stetson, leather belt and cowboy boots, put in two hundred that he took from his hat. A girl opposite me in plastic and safety-pins, clearly from Punk Rocker kitchen, added a few dimes. More than a hundred and fifty kitchens, from Lost Souls to Cornucopia, through Calm and the Gypsy Cafe, took turns to cook for the dinner circle. I had joined Everybody's and worked finding firewood and carrying water. The proceeds from Magic Hat, some ten to fifteen thousand dollars every mealtime for three weeks, went on food in the local village, two hours away down the mountain. The focalisers brought it back to Supply where kitchens would collect a share according to their numbers.

DINNER TIME

In 1992 this was the 20th annual gathering. They began after a Vietnam Seals veteran who, on leave in Haight Ashbury, had been hugged by three random hippies saying, "We love you, Brother." When he left the service he travelled the country telling of his vision for a community who would gather each year and celebrate life and pray for Whirled Peas. He made it happen. Fifteen hundred people turned up to the first gathering: he had expected maybe two hundred.

After the circle I sought out the little man in orange shorts. He had fierce twinkly eyes and said, "Welcome home, Brother. Be yourself!"

"Is that so easy?" I said.

"How hard do you want to make it?"

"How long will it take me?"

"How long do you want"

"How much practice will I need?"

"What practice did you have in mind? To meditate every day on what has caused you pain? To use that cause and that pain as a reference for present and future experience? How then can you experience the present and future without pain? ... leave it behind: in the past, where it belongs. Be yourself. Be yourself and live, live in the present moment as intensely as if running with your hair on fire...or stroll through life supremely at leisure. Or as you feel, in the moment, in the spaces between, in the void. Be yourself, always and in everything."

I saw him again, at a gathering in Australia. I waited to speak to him, gave him Namaste and put my hand on my heart.

"Thank you, Shantiji, thank you for your words."

He did not recognise me. Why should he: he must have seen and inspired thousands. "My words?"

"What you said in Colorado. To be myself."

"Ah, those words."

"Ever since then, every difficult situation I've found myself in, every decision I've had to take, and sometimes when I have just not known what to do, your words have echoed in my mind."

He seemed to stare into my soul. He said, "You've done it, haven't you."

"I thank you, Shantiji. You helped me be myself."

His fierce twinkly eyes filled. "No, you helped yourself. I can only recite words." And he turned away.

I saw him again, dancing in the Sunday drum-circle on Makena beach in Maui, still in the orange shorts. He sought me out.

"I remember you. You said I helped you."

"You did. I still think of you and thank you in my heart."

"Are you doing OK?" The fierce twinkle had faded.

"Well enough," I said. "I have the life I want."

"Plenty of money then?"

"I don't have money, Shantiji, only enough for my needs, which are few. I have no possessions to speak of. One travel a year, no expensive tastes, no drink, no drugs. I live simply, teach meditation, shiatsu."

"So you can't help me out?"

"What do you need? I'll help with what I can."

"A quarter-million would solve all my problems."

Sitting quietly in the Tao Garden some months later I noticed a young man giving me the keen interested glances of someone seeing someone he thought might be a highly evolved spiritual being. I was cultivating the long hair and dreamy countenance of one with his mind on higher things and accordingly bedecked with bracelets and bangles, ear-ring and beads, clothed in ethnic trousers, sandals and one of those guru-shirts that lend an aura of peace and serenity. I'd recently attended a Vipassana retreat too, so must have looked pretty holy, perhaps even halogenically enlightened.

His bow, almost a walking prostration, as the young man approached showed the immense measure of respect with which he had decided to endow the presentation of me that I was offering the world at the time. His first words, uttered as if in a cathedral or the presence of a cathedral spirit, caressed my ego.

"May I speak with you?" he said, sounding American. Graciously I inclined my head. He continued, "I feel I can learn many things from you."

"How can I help you?" I said in a conversational tone and my normal English accent.

His eyes, lowered until he heard my voice, looked up startled, "Where are you from?" he asked.

"London, England," I replied.

His face fell as fast as he stood upright. "London? England?"

I tried the gracious nod again but it bounced off the wall of indignation forming around him as he stared angrily at my clothes, my hair, bracelets, beads and sandals, and took a step back.

"I thought you might have been a...from.... I thought I might have learned something from you," he said like a child to a broken promise.

I was curious. "Learned something like what?"

"Something, oh I don't know, wise stuff. Yeah, some wisdom."

"Maybe you have," I said after him, as he walked away under his disappointed cloud, seeking a distant truth.

You know what they say: nowadays the westerners wear the robes, the gurus drive the Mercedes.

I got my hair cut, chucked the ornamentation. I bought cool gear in Waikiki boutiques, signed up for NLP with Richard Bandler. Nobody mistakes me for a medicine-man any more.

"As I see it, there's no Buddha, no living beings, no long ago, no now. If you want to get it, you've already got it-- it's not something that requires time. There's no religious practice, no enlightenment, no getting anything, no missing out on anything. At no time is there any other Dharma than this. If anyone claims there is a Dharma superior to this, I say it must be a dream, a phantom."

THE ZEN TEACHINGS OF MASTER LIN-CHI,
TR BURTON WATSON

I had lived about half of the hundred years to which we are all entitled when I found myself sitting in that circle around an open fire in the mountains of Colorado, wondering how to live in a spirit of love, in this life, amid the slings and arrows of outrageous fortune.

The Rainbow Family's answer was simple: each day do Three Good Things:

Something for yourself

Something for another person

Something for your community

I added my own Daily Reality Check:

Am I doing what I want to do?

Am I being where I want to be?

Am I with who I want to be with?

Giving Shiatsu, expressing through my hands the unconditional love in my heart, is doing something for another person. By connecting with the universal love of Spirit, I do something for myself. By teaching Zen Shiatsu I am doing something for my community.

For me, that's a Yes, and I want to share that Yes with You. If an early seeker, you may find aspects of my practice of use. As a seasoned traveller you may have a little fun at my expense, thinking how much better your own practice or how superior your teacher. You will learn something, if only that you have nothing to learn. It doesn't matter really: we dance the same spiral with different steps as we follow the trail that leads to Spirit, by temple, church or beach. Mine was beach. I had designed a life to travel in the light, a life that included a lot of beach, the life that I live now but which I nearly lost before coming home to find my love, light of my life, and found my school.

*   *   *

Chapter 2
Death and Birth

Death and Birth

Full of London learning and Tokyo techniques I alighted on the Beach, the hippy isle of Koh Pha Ngan. Time to party! Having spent the Sixties creeping up on Her Majesty's enemies, giving 'em one for England and missing out on all the flower puff, thirty years on I explored a different kind of adventure.

The place was a true cliché paradise, beaches, hibiscus, bougainvillea, streams running from rocky jungle hillsides, people with inner laughter bubbling out, mushrooms on every menu. Just one short year ago I had a wife, a residence, a short haircut, wore straight shirts and worked in real estate. I'd been recommended the tea by Wayne, a wandering guitarist, who said "You don't go crazy on it, just a nice little trip." I guess that would apply to experienced trippers. I look and sound like a survivor of the Sixties, but of course I was faking it. After the tea I cross the palm-lined road to the Outback for a beer, thinking magic mushrooms over-rated and Castaneda a fraud. Then I noticed I was wrecked. Then I got enlightened. Then I understood. I understand everything I thought I had understood before. I understand the music now, all of it, from Sgt Pepper through acid rock to house. I understand the clothes and the colours and the language. And I understand the understanding.

This place should be closed down, or everybody sent here. It wasn't just an apple, Adam, was it? Now I understood the man at the Rainbow who, nearing the end of college, discovered acid, dropped out, turned on and tuned in, realising the joke is on everyone else.

The first party was at Coral Beach, violet light, fluorescent pictures, garage house. Black rain drenched me when I lay on the grass but I could turn it off. Stars swelled to just a few feet above earth and the sea rippled in psychedelic waves. People around me were suddenly naked, or suddenly clothed, and trees mobile. I could see my meridians singing in arms and hands. I was terribly thirsty, drank a lot of water and urinated often. I wanted to kick my legs and howl but could not let go enough to do that. It would have been an uncool thing to do. Now I know what cool is!

I danced through the night. We danced in rows, we danced like marchers. Watchers sat in ranks, staring at the dancers or out to sea at the darkness at the edge of the world. People fell where they sat, open-mouthed, gashes and patterns of luminous paint on faces and bodies. Puck danced like a squirrel around the edges, hands weaving a dive, face painted like an elf, a Red Indian elf, prancing, dancing and grimacing.

My lips are numb, jaw-muscles tight. Sky and stars rise and fall like a moving canopy. Stars peek from palm fronds. The sky lightened, I felt untripped and practised Qigong. The power flowed strong, between my hands. I could gather it from the earth with ease. I could shake in the Kamba dance I learned at fifteen. My bare feet on the grit felt like velvet pads. I could leap like a Masai. A girl in a short white skirt danced, inhaler stuck in a nostril. I don't think it was Vicks. She danced from loudspeaker to loudspeaker battering herself with din. A boy with golden hair and a gold-streaked body danced like a Sun Prince and a girl who could have been his sister, blonde hair smeared across her face, danced with all her limbs. A tall impassive woman patterned in body paint of many colours gyrated in the same spot for hours or minutes. Four men with the look of the desert leaped around a centre-pole luminous with red, purple and yellow.

I felt a strong and beautiful sense of relief that at last I had done it. Now I knew what I had not known before.

Between full-moon parties I earned mushroom-money teaching shiatsu on the beach. Spirit lurked in an enlightened woman of Israel.

"Full of yourself, more like," said Yael. "Your head is so far up your arse I'm surprised you can blink. Every word rehearsed, every movement contrived, fitting your mind-of-samurai hand-of-mother bullshit. You are playing a part, playing apart, where is your heart?" Twenty-four going on a thousand, waves of auburn hair, seagreen eyes, boyfriend with third-dan black belt, she lived every moment as though it were her last.

"Your shiatsu is like one of those Kyoto gardens: completely perfect, completely artificial. Let it go. Just follow your hands. You can re-learn to trust and to love, as I did, as you did as a kid. So Life happens, so what? Its different for each of us and the same for all." She knew of the personal life I had left broken in England. I knew of her discharge from the army and year of bedridden depression before recovering alone in the deserts of Sinai.

"You grew up learning to survive by copying and pleasing, Relearning needs nothing more than to be yourself. Find, free your spirit. Feel the love, where things begin."

I had time, then, lying in the shade of coconut palms, to read and reflect on the beginnings, mine and the therapy I love, on stories of the Yellow Emperor of ancient China who, creating foreplay techniques for his harem of 1,200 wives and concubines, found they also worked for healing. On the psychologist in modern Japan who devised a shiatsu protocol, and the Westerners who institutionalised it. Each played out their elemental role, from the Caring of Earth to the Organisation of Metal.

My own story nearly ended there, on that beach, under those palms. Too many mushrooms, not enough water, too much dancing, from midnight until the sun was high. Some still danced, in the pools of their shadows. At breakfast a man I did not know filled a chillum and asked if I had enjoyed my flight. I went to Leela Beach, the sacred grove of the goddess, and lay on the sand and swam in the sea. Then it hit me and I crashed and burned in the noonday sun, a mad dogged Englishman who didn't know when to stop.

Heavy sticky eyes opened to a vision of an angel beside me, rolling a spliff. Had we danced? My mind shot back to another life, the Haymarket Theatre, Andre de Shields dancing and singing, "I dreamed about a reefer that was five miles long," and drew in a deep breath of hot harsh smoke into a black red dark suddenly crowded with friends, lovers, business associates, family, everyone I had ever known. I saw my son in the future, raging across the world, my daughter recovered from addiction, rosy-cheeked and chubby in blue gingham, playing with two chubby children.

Huang-Ti, the Yellow Emperor, codified the theory behind the therapy. Treatment, from acupuncture to herbs, he decreed, should vary according to the life-style, environment and location of his subjects. For those dwelling in the mild climate of the central regions who were "able to obtain a varied diet without great exertion" massage was recommended to harmonise the elements of Fire, Earth, Metal, Water and Wood and thus maintain spiritual, energetic and physical health – and the interest of however many partners.

The images gave way to a tunnel of light. This, I found myself thinking at some level far removed from whatever reality I was in now, is not a good time. Or was it? I had no ties any more, no responsibilities to anyone, really.

"Are you ready?"

Why not? It has to happen some time and here was ideal. I was experiencing a new feeling, quite extraordinary. There was no fear, no regret, no sadness, no anger, no pain, no sorrow, no apprehension.

Everything felt perfectly right, at true peace. It was, I felt, unconditional happiness and to it there was no end. I was coming into a community of love and peace. I have no need to search, no need to wander, I was at home, eternal rest and peace in the love of the universe, my family and humankind. I thought of the happiness I had been given on earth, and the happiness I had given. Everything was beautiful.

"I am ready."

My body was closing down. The back of my throat, my tongue, the roof of my mouth and inner cheeks had dried out. My heart had slowed and dried. I could not feel or hear any beat. My lungs were collapsed and still. The light faded. I had accepted death. My soul readied itself to shuffle off. Below, the body lay empty.

"Do you want to go?"

I was ready but not willing because, on earth, I was in this paradise. "I want to make love again. I want to fall in love. I want to be in love."

My eyes flickered. I saw the sun and the palm tree, breathed in sunlight between my eyebrows and knew she would always be there, shining and smiling, giving light and life. With my mind's eye I looked inward and upward to a point at the top of my head, between my skull and my scalp. My crown opened to the sky, the stars and planets, the galaxies and constellations of the visible universe. I saw myself, standing in space, feet on the earth, head in the stars, sun in my navel, moon in my kidneys. The North Star opened to the universe beyond the visible, white mountain reflected in a crystal lake, an ancient healing forest, the sun in the ocean, fire blazing under water.

Local healing traditions evolved across the "Middle Kingdom" (between Heaven and Earth) and its spheres of influence, from Tibet to Japan, Siberia to Siam. Earth medicine flourished among the Fang Shi – Masters of the Formula, barefoot healers, witches, wizards and shamans. Under the Han and successive dynasties religious and magical Taoism emerged, peacefully co-existing with behavioural Confucianism, until the Northern Wei saw the rise of Buddhism and persecution of the shamans.

Healing became politicised.

Immortality being considered the logical outcome of good health, Chinese alchemists sought an Elixir for their Emperors, retaining a few drops for themselves. External alchemy lost its appeal when it did for a few courtiers and kings as well as a number of alchemists.

I looked downwards and inwards to my internal universe, my inner space, and there saw chaos as planets clashed. My spirit was like a man caught halfway out of his pyjamas. I left it to come back in its own way. I lay inside my skull, behind my nose. It was like being in an infrared bath. I looked at the inside of the bone, inside the cavity of my skull. I saw my teeth from behind and felt my tongue. I opened my eyes to feel the atmosphere of earth. The sun shone between clouds and warmed my face. From my place inside my head I could see out. The girl lay beside me, looking away. I went down to my fingers. They could move but were uncoordinated. I went to my legs. No longer empty: I could move them.

The search continued. Physicians in the Tang Dynasty vivisecting condemned prisoners described flows of energy through certain invisible channels, which ceased at the moment of death. If this flow could be sustained…

I visited my organs, thinking to practise the meditation of the Inner Smile to help me return. It was like a battlefield in there. Heart was charred, lungs a forest of blackened twigs. Liver and gallbladder were screaming with anger. Stomach, spleen and pancreas were wiped out, kidneys exhausted. Intestines lay inert in heaps like sausage skins and bladder, flaccid. Sex was neutral, nothing, empty.

"I'm sorry," I said.

They spoke to me. "Will you look after us now?"

"Yes."

"Will you do this again?"

I wanted to reassure them but they waited for the truth.

"I don't know."

I asked them if they would stop functioning and kill me if I did it again. They said, "We don't know. What happens, happens."

In the long dark silence a tremor touched my heart and a whisper woke my lungs. From a deep well of healing power moisture seeped back into the leathery tongue and numb lips.

Under Chairman Mao so-called Traditional Chinese Medicine (TCM) synthesised local and traditional approaches and purged the spiritual aspects, overlooking the less obvious magical which had been absorbed into orthodoxy as Five Elements. By the late 1950s standardised TCM was practised alongside dialectically materialist and politically correct western medicine, in the hospitals of a new China.

In modern times things happen fast: 1977 saw the Japanese psychologist Shizuto Masunaga and his student Wataru Ohashi develop a complex set of protocols integrating psychotherapeutic thought, meridian connection and physical pressure. Masunaga described how to induce the phenomenon that occurs between meridian points under pressure, and published it as *Zen Shiatsu – how to harmonise Yin and Yang for better health*. By making his name and system synonymous with Zen Shiatsu Masunaga reinforced the trend towards standardisation but in the post-war restoration of Japan the rival and even more rationalistic Namikoshi system, based on western neurology, became the one officially recognised in Japan.

I gave up the mushrooms. I had put the money aside to buy them, calculating how far my budget would extend to cover two-parties-a-week's worth. I was going through all the processes one of my rehab-clinic patients described, of thinking about going to the dealer, the high of anticipation, entering the dealer's house and sitting among the waiting customers, all the conversation around the drugs, of being invited into the private room, the VIP treatment of a habitual user, a regular customer, of going home thinking about what was in her handbag, taking the hit, looking forward to the effect, imagining it, waiting and, then, surrender. All over so soon but not so soon over as the blind goddess resumed her domination of every waking moment.

All I had to do in Haad Rin was walk into the cafe and order a glass of 'special' tea or a 'special' pancake, affordable, available and if not quite legal nobody cared on an island of traditional sanctuary for fled assassins of the Thai mafia and their supply-lines.

Shiatsu went West, welcomed by the eclectic materialists of the New Age. Yin, Yang and Zen, it involved touch, was supported by a suitably complex theory, was said to alleviate symptoms of many chronic conditions resistant to orthodox medicine and reduce the need for medication. Described as a Japanese form of physiotherapy by certain Western Schools, the intuitive loving-touch practised by barefoot blind healers wearing red headbands became the subject of theses and dissertations by earnest people in white.

The gap between rational/physical and traditional/spiritual began to close with the publication in 1988 of *Hara Diagnosis - Reflections on the Sea.* Matsumoto & Birch wrote of the flicker of life, the moving Qi between the kidneys, and explored the connections between Eastern and Western medicine. In 1989 at the Columbia Hotel in London Dr Motoyama and his Qi-machine demonstrated energy flowing through the connective tissues at 1.5 volts – hey, presto! energy is real, meridians exist! But among the dignitaries present, representing interests from scientific to esoteric, were those who feared an end to their mystique.

The Spirit of Love struck in the spring of '93. I had followed Yael to New York, roller-bladed through Central Park, stood with her in the

Peace Garden, looked across the world from the Empire State and broken bread at Friday night dinner. She left to join her black belt in Tokyo, telling me to meet her in Sinai later in the year. I returned to London and booked a flight into Egypt before falling in love and giving birth to the Zen School of Shiatsu. One of my growing number of ex-sisters-in-law had offered me a temporary nest where, one morning from the stairs down to breakfast I stopped, caught in my breath. I did not know Nicola had any friend so beautiful as the honey-blonde girl standing, four-year-old at her side, looking at the guinea-pig cage.

Our school was born out of love and my need to earn my living. I moved into Sheralee's flat and became Jade's Dad. We leased a synchronistically available big light studio in the East-West Centre. Shiatsu-related techniques had multiplied in the 80's and early 90's with the development of such as Ohashiatsu – Touch for Love, Shizuko Yamamoto's Barefoot Shiatsu, Macrobiotic Shiatsu, Mantak Chia's Chi Nei Tsang now recognised as Hara Shiatsu, Five-Element Shiatsu, energy-shiatsu – kiatsu, water-shiatsu or watsu, even tantric: tanatsu. There was room for one more.

Notices nailed to tree trunks had gathered my first crop of students to the Coconut Theatre on the sacred beach. There I began what evolved into a true Zen approach. Of one thing I was sure: I would not teach shiatsu the way I had been taught, with lectures and notes, explanations and demonstrations. I nailed new notices to processed trees: Time Out and, on Lee's advice, the Big Issue.

"But that's for homeless people," I protested, "They couldn't afford the fees. We have London rent to pay."

"Homeless people sell the Big Issue," she said. "Compassionate people buy it."

For the first five years of the Zen School, in fact until the Internet began to replace paper advertising, half of all our new students came from those ads in the Big Issue. The Spirit of Compassion has its own rewards.

Potential for harmony between the main approaches, Masunaga-Zen, Five-Elements and TCM was illustrated in 1995 by Carola Beresford Cooke in *Shiatsu Theory & Practice*. Then, in 1996, the English Zen Shiatsu Master, Simon Fall, inspired a return to the Source with *As Snowflakes Fall, Shiatsu as Spiritual Practice*. Realisation dawned: its not all just finger-push!

My shiatsu-parallel year at Teacher Training College had shown me a new spirit abroad in the world of education: learning by discovery. Blended with the techniques of Harvard Business School and the apprentice tradition of the Taoist Masters, this made for a unique approach to shiatsu as a learning-and-teaching experience.

Two years after Fall, the American acupuncturist, Lonny Jarratt, published *Nourishing Destiny, the Inner Tradition of Chinese Medicine* reviving the spiritual origins excised by Mao's dialectical materialists. Shiatsu in the West was ready to enter the new millennium. But the shadow of European bureaucracy threatened English freedom to practise, since the repeal of the Witchcraft Act in 1951, any complementary therapy without restriction or, indeed, qualification.

On the principle that if more than two Englishmen gather they start a club British institutionalism proliferated. Playing politics in the race for orthodoxy and acceptance by what they perceived as the Establishment, Shiatsu organisations vied for authenticity with regulation, examination, assessment, accreditation, validation and moderation in apparent belief that more rules would attract a greater membership with a louder voice in the meridians of power, not to mention subscription income.

Competition intensified. Rumours of poaching rippled through the bazaars. Databases disappeared to resurface under clouds of denial in rival offices. While older organisations stagnated in vested interests, elitism and exclusivity, nouveau upstarts canvassed bewildered students and practitioners with the relentless enthusiasm of a time-share seller. Fragmentation ruled in the world of gentle healing until Tom

Litten, a former trades-union organiser whose love of Shiatsu equalled his passion for politics, attempted to gather the rivals under the aegis of the General Shiatsu Council. Regulation became the buzz. Could we field a unified team in the game of Europe?

Most people coming into Shiatsu training are grown-ups who want to learn something new: to heal others, heal themselves, put their compassion to work, wonderful beings who, passing through this wonderful world, want to do something different while still honouring their commitments and responsibilities.

They come from other lives, perhaps with children, probably work for their living, and have taken responsibility for themselves. They are already motivated, sometimes inspired, always interested. Some have the support of parents or partners and can dedicate themselves full-time to their learning while others can spare only a few hours every week or month. Our teachers offer learning-experiences of more than technique, skill and knowledge; help them know themselves, honour themselves as they are rather than trying to fit into someone else's idea of what they should be; to find their way into being a practitioner, a Shiatsu person, with a sense of their own empowerment and worth, in their own time, at their own pace.

Our system of start-when-you-like continuous enrolment and attend-when-you-like self-responsibility drew the comment from one of my former teachers, "It won't work here."

How often had I heard that in my life?

Who are we to say what to teach or how to train, when there are manuals and videos from Carl Rogers to John Cleese on how to do it? Whatever the field, the principles are the same and we are all fingers on the same hand. Why have an application form? What more do you need than name, address and course fee? What matter their age or what else they've done in their life? Who are we to judge their fitness or otherwise to learn shiatsu? Who are we to judge?

In the tradition of Zen, a student is responsible for his or her own learning. Does it matter if they qualify this year or next, if they want time out to go travelling, have a baby, take in a year at another school, work abroad, get through a confidence-crisis, bereavement, marriage or divorce?

Instead of demonstrations we facilitate discussion groups around the principles of treatment: pressure, contact, connection, sensitivity. We ask each student to invent a treatment of their own on, for example, the back of the body, or the side, or the front. How amazing – they invent what we would have taught! But what they invent is theirs, learned by discovery and now owned, knowledge born of experience.

Instead of lectures we post themes, setting assignments of questions, thoughts and ideas. Students come ready to talk about their learning experience while the facilitator finds the gaps. This is both challenging and inspirational, but some students tend to overdo it so we issued a health-warning: more than three hours preparing an assignment can seriously damage enthusiasm.

Above all knowledge, technique and Intended Learning Outcomes, we follow the ebb and flow of the force known as Qi, bioelectromagnetic energy or energy-intelligence, throughout the organ-meridian networks. Our approach to shiatsu combines the wisdom of the Tao with the Beginner's Mind of Zen, trusting in the perfection of now, however it should manifest. We teach the caring touch of love, drawing down Heaven Qi to cleanse and Earth Qi up to heal.

"Zen opens our eyes to the greatest mystery as it is daily and hourly performed; it enlarges the heart to embrace eternity of time and infinity of space in its every palpitation; it makes us live in the world as if walking in the garden of Eden."

D. T. SUZUKI

---

*   *   *

Chapter 3
Working Zen

Working Zen

Old-fashioned school-learning programmed me into accumulating knowledge before putting it into practice, which was how I was first taught shiatsu. We went to lectures where a teacher wrote meridian theory with squeaky chalk on a blackboard to the sound of traffic. I could not even look out the windows as I did when a child, day-dreaming beyond the green meadows and shaded woods until a cuff round the ear returned me to the indoors. As a teenager I would rather go downtown and hang out in coffee bars. I have since read that education and upbringing are supposed to instil a powerful urge to succeed. I remember my mum sitting on the edge of my bed one morning, looking fondly at me and saying "You have just the right face for a head of school," just a few weeks before I was expelled at fifteen. Fifty years on, a TV critic wrote, "North...dressed up properly, might have looked the perfect Anglican archbishop."

After three years of bumming around Nairobi, sleeping in Jeevanjee gardens, stealing cars and being James Dean, hitch-hiking to Algiers to join the French Foreign Legion until picked up by blondes a few miles towards Nakuru, doing odd jobs and begging on the streets, I was caught for the last draft for military service in Kenya. I had expected to join up with three friends of the same age but they were dead, riding motorbikes too fast round corners on dirt roads and round tables of cafe terraces. Johnny and Brian killed each other playing chicken. Al borrowed a Land Rover and drove it off a cliff. I never really did get to grips with savings and pensions later in life while in those yang-gang days of youth most of us fulfilled our expectations to live fast and die young. Living in the moment: training for Zen practice. I didn't know it then.

Jay, the other survivor of our biker gang, had been called up the year before and we got drunk in the billiards bar of the Queens Hotel as he passed on handy hints for military survival.

"Keep you nose clean. And your rifle." I took half that advice.

The Kenya Regiment trained white men to be officers, in the event of war, in the Kings African Rifles: white officers with black privates. Despite getting locked up now and again for assaulting my superiors, hating the discipline but loving the energy, I found a spiritual home. I met men who lived in the bush, made their living hunting or farming, doing what they loved. I learned to shoot, to ride a horse, to follow tracks, to see without being seen. In the Young Brave phase of my life I was young, and brave.

A brief return to being a civilian where I could walk out of a dozen jobs without being court-martialled convinced me to sign on again and enjoy a few years of paid adventure, professional in South Arabia and romantic around the Mediterranean reciting St Augustine's prayer, "Lord, give me chastity. But not just yet." I even made it to Algiers, a newly commissioned army officer aboard a Royal Navy frigate, sent to represent our country at their Tenth Anniversary of the Beginning of the Struggle for Independence, celebrated with an Islamic reception: halal lamb, mountains of fresh fruit, no alcohol, and the Military Attaché's nanny in the corridor.

A restless spirit, the prospect of peacetime, garrison duties in north-west Europe and drinking in the afternoons drove me to escape. I transferred to the Gurkhas, Nepalese mercenaries who worshipped Kali, Goddess of Death, terrifier of the ignorant and protector of the enlightened. It was my first real meeting with a glimpsed world.

It was also where I first learned to teach, army stuff: weapon skills, drills and suchlike; later, tactics and strategies, current affairs and military history. It felt a natural kind of thing to do. I seemed to have a talent for putting things across and keeping going until satisfied the learning had been absorbed and could be applied in real life and, of course, death, the business of armies. Most Gurkha soldiers had had no education at home in the Himalayas. It was one of their motivations for spending time in the British, Indian and Chinese forces. They had much to teach me, about working with a different culture, about respect, about myself.

My father was a teacher. He taught French, the language of his ancestors. Retired, in his eighties, he would still get letters from pupils of half-a-century before. When he died we had 80 years of teaching between us. My son is a teacher. This is our ancestral Qi. We discovered, through our different trainings in different space-times, that state-of-the-art, cross-modular educational methods fit well with the Zen approach. Learning by discovery, entertaining and challenging, could be straight out of the Zen Book were there such a thing.

The Zen approach to Shiatsu has no religious affiliation yet in it I found a profound spiritual practice. The spiritual aspect of Shiatsu is the essence of Zen. How do we apply the practice of Zen to the practice of shiatsu? As in Zazen – seated Zen meditation – the structure or posture is the key to understanding the connection, finding that true spirit.

"...it is impossible to understand if one does not practice. If you practice you get back to what is original, to complete purity. That is satori. Not a special state, not a condition of transcendent consciousness."

QUESTIONS TO A ZEN MASTER: TAISEN DESHIMARU

The difference between Zazen and Zen Shiatsu is the presence of another person: your Receiver, with whom you are physically connected by your hands. For this other presence, you add to your physical connection the spirit of Love.

Do you need to think loving thoughts then, as you lean with natural perpendicular pressure?

It is enough to acknowledge the love in your heart and let everything else go by.

> *"In Zen what you must do is let your thoughts pass by. As soon as a thought arises, let it go. If money comes, or sex, or food, or Buddha or God or Zen, let it go...concentrate on your posture and let everything else go by."*
>
> *TAISEN DESHIMARU*

Even in the spiritual way of Zen Shiatsu, a hands-on therapy to help others and connect with Spirit, before going near a textbook our students must show they can give an intuitive treatment. Shiatsu, at the basic physical level, is a simple manual skill underpinned by a complex body of theory. Allowing a new student to first develop the practical skills means he or she can learn to move around the body or move the body around, without just yet having to think of which meridian to work or what point is good for what condition, or what Oriental Theory model might influence treating, say, dysmenhorrea. Treatments work with Intention: Mu-Shin, or Empty Mind, free of expectation.

> *"When you expect something, when you aim at something, right there you dilute your energy; you split your energy, you split your attention and it becomes more than the place of yin and yang. You do not only divide, but create the problem."* *TAIZAN MAEZUMI*
> A Hawaiian might say, *"The unaimed arrow never misses."*

It took me a little time to get my head round Zen as a spiritual yet non-religious practice. A Catholic childhood had given me insights into mysticism but generally put me off religion, which, until middle age, I equated with organised belief systems. What, I wondered, was the difference between the Zen approach and the religious approach, between the spiritual way of Zen, Zen Buddhism and devotional

Buddhism? The Zen word is itself a Japanese pronunciation of the Chinese word *ch'an*, from the Sanskrit *dhyan*: meditation.

The Zen philosophy evolved, through assimilation of Taoist concepts, beyond the duality – cause and effect – of traditional religious Buddhism which, like Judaism and later Christianity and Islam, clung to the idea of struggle: Good vs. Evil, Right Way vs. Wrong Way, leading inevitably to division within their belief systems.

The imported belief systems we have adopted over the millennia spring from the environments which enabled them to take root, grow, flourish and spread. The harsh environment of the desert where each day is a struggle for life, where extremes of heat and cold exist under a huge sky, home of an angry god who lays down laws of behaviour. Compare with the climates and seasons of the temperate zone, Europe, North America and much of Asia, where what are now described as the 'Old Ways' evolved, nurtured by spring, warmed in summer, harvested in late summer, conserved in fall, rested in winter: human in harmony with nature.

The patriarchal and judgemental religions of the Middle East became the new ways of the Old World. They brought out the competitive acquisitive nature of man, the relish for conflict and combat reflected – too gentle a word – in modern society. And the white man's thunder-god carried these divisive ways into societies unprepared.

"Seek not the truth, nor cherish opinions." Zen, like Taoism, understanding that Right and Wrong depend on the view of the observer, embraces Harmony: Heaven and Earth instead of Heaven and Hell.

I saw a poster on a bus stop in London, a huge photograph of Wembley Stadium, with the caption 'Is this Heaven and Hell?' – whether you supported the winning or losing team. In reality it is just a football field: a piece of earth. I thought the ad so clever and so obvious I missed the point of what they were advertising.

Learning the language and concepts of Oriental Medicine, novices listen to the more experienced. Tutors offer encouragement without correction until the new student has passed a Practical assessment, typically after three months, and completed specified reading in their own time. And then they dive in, preparing assignments, learning everything at once.

"It seemed like I was drowning," said Duncan, a scientist whose pre-shiatsu career was in civil engineering, "until I decided I rather liked the feeling and just let the tide wash over me."

My own early learning was centred on the convenience of the teachers, who delivered anatomy in the first year, physiology in the second and pathology in the third; classical meridians before extensions. It took me a very long time to integrate the separate streams into an ocean of understanding and I was determined to teach my own grown-up students to become effective practitioners, rather than writers of theses. One does not shiatsu with a pen, I would say, remembering Master Suzuki's gruff "No notes!"

Now our modules blend western anatomical systems of muscles, organs and bones with meridian routes. Anatomy modules require an understanding of the related organ-meridian networks, while Pathology includes choosing appropriate use of acupoints as well as considering possible recommendations in terms of life-style, exercise, meditation, outlook and diet.

And we abolished written examinations. Of what help is it to be able to answer the easy questions first and do the difficult later when faced with a challenging situation in the clinic with a real live person needing help, on the mat, in the moment? Surely, I thought, the knowledge must live in the hands, the body, the energy field? Everyone who drives a car is capable of complex multi-tasking involving knowledge of theory and its application in practice. What is so different? Rules of the road, rules of practice, ways of doing things. As long as we know enough western medical terminology to understand what patients are talking about when referred by a doctor, to convert from that paradigm into a hands-on treatment based on oriental medicine, and to explain to the client what we are doing and why, with love, clarity, and the simplicity of Zen.

With its clear and simple approach uncluttered by shibboleth, ritual or religious cant, Zen offered a refuge from the institutionalisation and sectarian divisions of Buddhism and the tendency of many Buddhists to treat the Buddha as a kind of deity – He who said there is no God – and from the frustratingly unworkable concept of duality which condemns every Buddhist to *'innate dissatisfaction with this life' (The Dalai Lama's Book of Wisdom, HH the Dalai Lama).*

In the same spirit, we wanted to offer relief from the standard, memorised routines of conventional western shiatsu teaching of the kind I had experienced. Where are the standard routine people, I asked?

The simplicity of the Zen approach, a doctrine of No-Mind: *"a way of seeing with a clarity free of preconception, of letting go duality" (The Zen Doctrine of No-Mind, D T Suzuki)* allows for profound spiritual practice to inform and enhance our actions in this world, whether shiatsu, meditation, martial arts, or just plain living.

In the library at Dharamsala I had witnessed the debates, monks with mallas wrapped around biceps, robes round shoulders, arms free to gesticulate, arguing philosophical disciplines and such matters as the relative karmic consequences of killing a real person or of killing an imaginary person. I drifted off into thoughts of the origins, the words of Shakyamuni Buddha committed to writing four centuries after being spoken. So many words – fifty years of teachings compressed into eighty volumes of scripture.

"Enough," I imagined the rebel, Bodhidarma, declaring. "How can we gain merit picking to pieces such unlikely situations?"

"Then how are we supposed to understand the scriptures?" said the Rinpoche, the one aware of his previous incarnations.

"Dhyan. Meditate. Just do it," replied Bodhidarma, gathering his robe about him, crossing his legs into lotus and gazing at the foot of the wall.

Later he rose and walked through the snowy Himalaya passes into Tibet, to find the ideas of the Buddha enlivened there with demons and deities, dakhinis and bodhisattvas, sustained by hierarchical monasticism, entrenched in illusion, with form, ritual and ceremony.

"For illusion to exist it must be observed, therefore the observer exists," he mused, "who must be just as real as the illusion."

Wandering east along mossy trails, he felt thoughts and words clouding the moment of clarity. "It is only my own experience that is real to me, as is our own to each of us, as was his own to Shakyamuni. He tried to communicate this, but had to use words. Can we do without words, empty the mind of all experience?"

"Or let go searching," remarked Lao Tse, asleep by the wayside.

Bodhidarma stopped. "How do you know I seek?"

"You move, therefore you seek. Whatever it is, is already there. You know it, even if you cannot define or describe it. Do you dance?"

"Of course," replied Bodhidarma, "what spiritual teacher doesn't?"

The Patriarch and the Celestial Master circled in stately rhythm, singing to the rocky hills.

Sang Lao Tse: "Being in the ordinary way, strolling through life, supremely at leisure."

Responded Bodhidarma: "Living each day intensely, as if your hair were on fire!"

"Tis simple to understand but not to explain," trilled the Sage.

Bodhidarma slowed, a slight frown creasing the fearsome brow.

"The idea of seeing your face before you were born is actually quite hard to understand and cannot be explained at all."

"No understanding, no explanation," sang Lao Tse, "no thought, no talk,

just mystic quietism,

dancing or working,

healing or fighting,

loving or losing,

singing a song or sewing a seam,

coming or going, yet always at home."

"Ah," Bodhidarma beamed, "mystic quietism – sitting in meditation, contemplating koans."

Lao Tse grinned as he hopped around a stone "Just sitting, just living, its all meditation. Beyond definition, beyond description, beyond using words to promote the idea of no-words. Ch'an. Just do it. "

"Long speech," said the Patriarch.

"You're getting the idea," said the Sage, mounting an ox, "you only need words to heal, to comfort and to teach." He sat still on its back as the ox plodded away, calling over his shoulder, "let good fortune jump on you."

Bodhidarma strolled into the rising sun, contemplating the moment of not thinking, of connection with reality. When you start to think, he thought, you're back in mind and the moment has become of the past. Our lives are spent heading for the future, away from the past, while the present slips by unnoticed. Our lives are spent. We spend our lives. We spend. And yet to stop the mind thinking is like asking the heart to stop beating. Is no-mind a philosophy? Is not-thinking a discipline? There must be more to it than that!

He met the Yellow Emperor by way of the Dragon Gate and asked him "Why are we here?"

"Are we here? and if we are, why not? Do we need a reason? What reason could there be? To sit in meditation until arms and legs wither? To pray to a god? To renounce society or to live in society? To live right? What is right?"

With a mental shrug Bodhidarma gave up, and watched the dawn of subtle clear light and heard at last the silent thunder: "Neither seek the truth nor cherish opinions. Zen. Just get on with it."

A student asks, "How do you know when you've got it? What are the signs and symptoms?"

I reply, "You may notice a sense of calm in your heart, satisfaction in your soul, peace in your mind, your body finding its own balance. A sense of clarity, of not wanting; of containment, of your inner resources and deep healing power; of immunity from negative influence; of ability to help others without depleting yourself. Everything feels right, heaven and earth in place, you between: in Union with Spirit. This I promise you: those in your presence, under the touch of your gifted grace, will notice before you do."

Another asked," Who was your best teacher?"

They all raced through my mind and crossed the line together. "You can learn from everyone," I answered, full of correctness and positivity, "even from – especially from – those who seem to be teaching what not to do and how not to do it."

Question and answer were general. Had he asked who was my best shiatsu teacher I would have said Nigel Dawes who made me want to continue learning after I left one of those officious 'only this way is right' shiatsu schools: yes, they exist even in the world of gentle healing. My best Taoist teacher was and still is Mantak Chia whose genius lies in teaching ancient stuff to modern people, rendering esoteric Taoist concepts comprehensible to us westerners with our academic approach and intellectual education.

My best meditation teacher was Roger Evans whose teaching changed my life: after one weekend with him in 1972, my chronic headache (I was on 60 tablets a day) and insomnia vanished, as did the annual winter bronchitis, and vanished for ever. My best life-teacher was Yael from whom I learned the most of everything in the shortest time.

My best love-teacher was Sheralee. I didn't need teaching to learn to love her but she taught me that sometimes its better to leave aside the rigours of the Zen way and give a little more help, a little more love, to people trying to help themselves.

As teachers of teaching technique, I would choose the team of Richard Bandler, founder of NLP, Paul McKenna and John La Valle. Their teachings have inspired and informed every aspect of my work. Let us do some of that work now so you too can learn to make your living doing what you love.

"Our life is shaped by our mind; we become what we think. Suffering follows an evil thought as the wheels of a cart follow the oxen that draw it. Joy follows a pure thought like a shadow that never leaves."

THE BUDDHA

---

*   *   *

Chapter 4
Learning by Heart

Learning by Heart

Can we share some ideas? You are you and I am me – as different as our DNA, and here to learn from each other. The feeling I used to get when another shiatsu or meditation book came out: Goodness, how wonderful, wish I had done that, don't they know a lot, wish I knew that much and could put it so clearly. Then you realise you know most of it anyway, but somewhere buried in the pages you find one or two new ideas that can help you with what you are already doing and doing so well. The more you read the more you have to, like mining for gold. Time was, a former time when to make money was the morning motivation for getting out of bed, when I speculated in the shares of goldmines.

I would wait for the Moodys, Reuters and Extel envelopes to drop on my doormat packed with information on mines in Australia and South Africa. A mine's productivity was the cost of getting the gold out of the earth. The cost equated to the number of tons of ore that had to be mined to extract one ounce. I was only interested in uneconomical mines that had closed down in years gone by when the gold price was low. Shares in working mines with ounces per ton were too expensive for me.

The gold-price edged up. Some economic crisis or threatened war triggered those extremes of the human condition that make us flee into the solid portable touchable beautiful metal, ultimate means of exchange anywhere in the world – have you ever offered a fiver for goods in the Andes? Or a dollar for a pint in Mumbles on a Sunday?

The Americans have enshrined the state of man-made money, printing 'In God we trust' on their currency while safeguarding the constitutional right of atheists to disbelieve in that deity whilst worshipping the Almighty dollar. The Bank of England simply offers a Promise to pay on demand the sum of £x. What do you think you would get if you took your fiver in and demanded? Another fiver. And all Banks operate on the basis that ninetythree percent of their customers are not going to want all their money out at the same time, which is certainly true but does it mean those little black figures on your statement are what you have 'in the bank'? Of course not, but you do trust them to give you that amount – in promises – on demand. Because they tell you they can, because they know you're worth it.

You take my point: in times of uncertainty or turbulence some deep survival instinct drives us to trust only what we really believe in, and from Pharaoh to Fort Knox we have trusted gold. And when the gold price rises it restores profitability to uneconomical mines, making their shares worth having. Long before they reopen, those shares go up as the speculators dive in for a killing. I saw a little old mine called Witwatersrand Nigel jump from 9p to 12p overnight. I bought an option to buy a hundred thousand. If the price went down or didn't go up within two weeks I would have to drop the option and fork out twelve hundred pounds, which in 1972 I did not have a tenth of. As it happened I sold out at 60p within six days, keeping me in high-tension nail biting lifestyle.

I lost it gracefully over succeeding months of indulgence spiced with addiction to greed and fear. Of course I could not take the money and run! What gambler does? But I did learn useful things that helped me know myself better and help me now to understand others, for are we all not a mirror?

"The world is like a mirror, you see? Smile, and your friends smile back."

JAPANESE ZEN SAYING

It is all in the mind, and all in the touch. We touch gold; we feel what is real, what can buy us stuff when faith has fled. We feel reassured. We feel: eyes and ears can trick us but in touch we trust. Shiatsu is healing by touch. Earth, the Mother, soothes and comforts and takes away the pain. The Mother instinct is Love, the medicine of Heaven. The combination of Love and Touch is why people come to Shiatsu, whether to receive or to give. Whichever points you press or meridians you stretch, it is your intention that makes your treatment wonderful. Allow your instinct to form your intention and you will bring healing wherever you go.

As novice you learn to recognise instinct as your most powerful aid. Going intermediate and into theory, you educate instinct into intuition. Advanced, you can let go of the intellectual mind-set and follow your hands. As a mindful practitioner you use all the tools of the trade: Compassion, Intuition, Intention, Skill and Knowledge. An adept, you direct healing energy from Heaven into Earth. A master sits in the energy-field, open to all possibilities. At whatever level, the Giver of Shiatsu is giving Love, the energy of Heaven, through Touch, the energy of Earth; Mind and Body, connected by Spirit.

Our approach is holistic, a hands-on therapy to harmonise the flow of energy throughout the entire being: mind, body and spirit; to seek the underlying cause of conditions as well as relieving symptoms; to open our Receiver's awareness to the environment hosting the condition; to help facilitate our Receiver's healing while understanding Nature as the true healer, Shiatsu but an intermediary. I have been asked if belief is essential to the process. I ask the asker if he or she believes that the chair they are sitting on is supporting them.

Belief is not necessary because in this world of illusion who knows what to believe? One could start with truth, simplicity and love, but what are they? If you write on a piece of paper, 'the other side is the truth', turn it over and on the back write 'the other side lies', where then does the truth lie? Your truth can be your lie, your reality an illusion.

Between losing my gold-profits and driving a mini-cab I managed a nightclub and discovered the reality of illusion my very first night. Captains of industry, faces familiar from photographs in the financial pages, theatrical knights and, my God, a famous reforming clergyman still incredibly in his dog-collar (later I learned he liked being led in a real one), titillated by Janet Reger waitresses bearing bottles of Dom Perignon to velvet alcoves by a tiny stage where exotic dancers shed silks and satins and a floor of lissom hostesses whispered promises to pay through bought red lips in the ears of Alpha males with share-holders money to squander, in amounts to turn anyone communist. An escape from reality; or to it?

Simplicity? Running a property business when computers were beginning to show their usefulness, I bought a program to keep the accounts. I knew nothing about computers but was assured that this was a simple program, designed for a small business, and would do everything a book-keeper did but faster and cheaper. I opened the manual to the first instruction: open a batch file. Now that may have been simple for the programmer who wrote the manual, but for me? I re-hired the bookkeeper.

And Love? Well, there are enough kinds to choose from and enough to go round and make the world go round with it. In shiatsu, its what we do. Love from heart running out through hands. But where to put it? Educating intuition leads in to diagnosis, and diagnosis means tak-ing a position, making a judgement: not very Zen. But does it bene-fit your client to conclude that here you have a nice healthy person? Healthy they may be, and nice, but to focus your treatment you need to see their imbalances. Does this falsify the truth of following your hands with unconditional love and letting the healing happen? Or does it pinpoint a paradox?

The answer is not in your head. Getting out of your head and into your hands, absorbing theory into cellular memory, tells those hands where to go. Follow, notice where they take you, then look up the points, the meridian network, organ, back to the source, the condition and beyond, to the environment allowing that condition to seed, take root, grow and flourish. You have put your love to work and now have something constructive to share, to help your client heal at home.

My after-treatment recommendations, what I call my prescriptions, help clients participate in their self-healing: whatever we can do for them on the mat it is only they who can change what they do off it.

Intuition is the primary diagnosis; Intuition is the voice of Spirit. It pays to listen as I discovered one starless night when Spirit spoke in a narrow stony valley.

My platoon patrolled in darkness, visibility under ten feet. The opposition used such nights of the black moon to bury land-mines in our supply airstrip. Every dawn and again before any aircraft landed one of us expendable subalterns would drive the floor-armoured Land Rover up and down the hard sand, scanning for marks, up and down, waiting for a blast like a boot up the ass to lift the heavy vehicle skywards while the driver clung to hope and the roll-bar. It was a fast way of mine-clearance, taking but a few minutes, but risked the occasional limb or broken neck. The night patrol was to ambush the mine carriers on their way to lay their AVs in the runway.

As we entered the wadi I led up to the left, one step at a time along the slope, ready to open fire on the instant at any sound from the valley floor, knowing a hail of copper-coated lead would be the response to any sound from us. Both sides played the rules in that last of the civilised wars: by day we watched them ride their camels through the valley with impunity. Losing their immunity in the curfew from dusk to dawn they crept through on foot, silent robed men with heavy backpacks and light Kalashnikovs.

In desert darkness the eyes no longer have it. Ears pricked, with each step I lift my foot, lower it to the ground in front, feeling for loose stones through soft crepe soles. I shift my weight slowly forward, ready to lift off at the faintest beginnings of the first suspicion of noise. Behind me, the line of armed men is doing the same. Or so I thought.

A scuff of sound to the right swung me aiming into the night but even as my finger touched the trigger I froze with a shouted whisper. "don't shoot!" We hit the deck, hearts in thunder, stones scrunching like

Brighton beach, and heard an English curse from the darkness across the valley. I risked shouting another whisper: "Who's there?" knowing that if I'd been wrong the reply would be a bullet-storm: they would have no doubt where to fire.

"Sanders," came the voice of the rear section leader. He had fallen a few steps behind, enough to lose sight of the man in front of him, and veered off to the right, taking his eight men on a parallel course along the opposite side of the narrow wadi. What made me hold back? Two nights before, we had all loosed off at a sudden whirr of a nightbird's wings. Razor-sharp response meant staying alive. Accidents happened.

"I thought we were goners," he said, back in camp after we aborted the patrol. "Why didn't you open fire?"

In the instant between Sanders' desert-boot dislodging a stone and my first shout preventing a night of shattered lives, I had seemed to be over the valley, looking down as if through night-vision lenses (which weren't around then). Above the scene I saw they were my own troops in the killing zone.

"Intuition," I said. "Intuition overrode training."

Since those warrior days I have learned its value over and over again, so much so I now teach intuition as the primary diagnostic tool in Zen Shiatsu, the art of gentle healing. Listen to what your feelings are telling you, without questioning or trying to explain. It is not necessary always to act on what you feel. Simply observing what intuition says is a good beginning, both for training your awareness and for insights into your client. Making a note of these primal observations will help as you flow into more rationalistic diagnoses of Looking, Asking, Sensing and Touching. You may find confirmation as your practice develops of Intuition's power to go straight to the core of being...to reach the soul...the essence.

During my first few hundred treatments it became clear to me that while different diagnostic methods could give different results, tuning in to intuition sparked that flash of insight where you suddenly know what is right for that person you are treating at that time. The process of learning Zen Shiatsu informs your Intuition: spirit speaks in a language you understand. As an experienced practitioner you will appreciate the value of Intuition throughout subsequent diagnoses, hearing a client's hidden agenda behind their answers to questions, or feeling that something "isn't quite right" in the touching diagnosis.

While Intuition can happen the moment you know of the very existence of a person whether by email, phone-call or referral, the moment of truth is when you first set eyes on them. Appearance may or may not match their telephone voice. Be open to the power of this first impression. In life it can mean love at first sight (what's the other kind?) In shiatsu it is the beginning of the Looking Diagnosis.

What feature catches your attention? How are they built? How do they move? Carry out your Looking indirectly and under cover of Asking, Sensing and Touching. Steal glances rather than steel stares: a new client can be disconcerted by too penetrating a gaze. Camouflage your observation with a greeting: hugs and handshakes, from wet fish to python-grip, show insights into personality.

I'm cool

I'm hot!

You're cool

You're hot!

Come closer

Keep away!

I'm strong

I'm wobbly

I need to touch

I hate to touch

I'm independent

I'm needy

I'm gentle

I'm tough

I'm busy

I'm still

I need to be here

I need to get away

I love my body

I hate my body

I love your body – hey, back off!

Social interaction is Image Management. Peek through the facade in the unconsidered moments of Arrival. Asking if they would like to change with, "Would you like to change?" brings answers from 'Yes' to 'No' or 'What do you mean' as the brain copes with this double-edged question, different from the straightforward 'Would you like to get changed?' Or consciously use the penetrating gaze to apply a little extra pressure, head lowered and eyebrows raised like a Paxman, and saying 'Change!' (They may hand you coins.)

By placing your client under gentle stress, you glimpse the natural Spirit-element, to which people revert under pressure. Growing up we survive by copying and pleasing: presenting images that we think and hope will get us what we want. Sales persons are taught how to manage the image they present to a client in response to the image the client is presenting to them. The truth behind the impression leads to the sale, or for us, the healing. We can tune in to what our client-receiver-patient really needs. A known need is easier to fulfil than an unknown and observation eliminates guesswork. An obvious need finds its own healing.

They knew exactly what I needed in Pushkar. Parents dead, wife fled, my universe had fallen off. I travelled in search of peace, reconciliation for my soul, something to revive spirit, something. I had been warned of the rogues who would fleece me.

"Watch you don't get ripped off. The going rate for a blessing is sixty, top whack."

"You want blessing?' importuned an urchin, "very good blessing. Come, we make puja." He took me down broad white steps to the lake said to be formed from a tear of Lord Krishna. The ashes of Gandhi and Nehru had been scattered in its waters. Whisper has it that some ashes of the Great Soul were also thrown in the Ganges for the goodwill of Lord Shiva. Gods as jealous as any Greek or Norse play out their leela in the Hindu firmament. Pushkar has the only temple to Lord Brahma, the result of a spat with Shiva about who was the most powerful.

I began to feel scared as we stepped down to the Brahmin waiting by the waterside. He sat in lotus, shaven brown head gleaming in the sunlight, round red tikka between his eyebrows, soft brown eyes; white dhoti in folds around pudgy waist. He had a kind, serious face. On his mat I could see a small brass bell, a bowl, yellow flowers and candles. He handed me a tiny candle set in a flower.

"Think of your family," he said. My eyes filled.

"Your father and mother, your brothers and sister, your wife, your children, your grandson." My throat choked up.

"Think of your students, your teachers, your friends, of those you love and those who love you." I had told him nothing of myself and he knew everything. My tears streamed into the lake.

He rang the bell to draw the attention of the gods, and lit the candle. "Everyone is born, everyone dies. It is both ways. The born die, the dead are born."

He signed me to crouch on the lowest step. I could see pebbles beneath the clear water. "Put the candle on the water. As it floats away, speak the names of those you love, the dead and the born."

I did, with a voice that didn't work properly. The little candle floated away on its flower, burning down, the flower slowly sinking, until both were gone and, with them, the weight of sadness that had been crushing me. I had made peace with my spirit and of those I had lost, through death, divorce or alienation.

After a time, he took my hand and tied a coloured string around my wrist. I said, "What should I pay you?"

"Give what you have." I had small money, my beggar-fund, in one pocket, hundred-rupee notes in another, more hundreds in the money-belt under my clothing.

I said, "Isn't there a price? What do most people pay?"

He gestured with a round bare arm, around the round lake. "These white marble temples were built by Maharajahs, great kings who found solace in the blessing of Lord Brahma. Rich merchants endow the hotels and free hostels for the poor in the streets behind. Each gives what they have."

My flight alone had cost more than most Indians would see in a lifetime. I reached into my large-money pocket, pulled out two hundred rupees and folded them into the bowl, thinking of my generosity over the going rate of sixty, top whack. He nodded and said, "This is your offering to Lord Brahma. Now you may clean your karma further with a gift for his servant."

"How much would his servant like?"

"Give what you have." Would it be insulting, I thought, to offer him less than I gave his god, or disrespectful to his god to give more to the servant? I compromised with an equal sum. They could sort out any differences between them, he and his deity.

"Now you may buy food for my family."

"How much is that?" I said, guessing the answer.

"Give what you have." I knew one could live on less than twenty pence a day for food and lodging. From the array of blessings on his mat he was looking at a good day. I could give another hundred without getting out my money-belt and showing my riches but it would clean out my daily budget. What had he given me that was worth a day's money? Would I, would any tourist, inconvenience themselves? Had I survived my gambling years by betting only what I could afford?

His face had not changed, his eyes not left mine. I felt my every thought being written on my forehead for him to read, observe and diagnose. I gave him my last hundred from the big-money pocket. It still added up to less than a fiver. He asked no more and I was content. We both got satisfaction.

The string bracelet, my 'Pushkar passport' saved me from importuning urchins: it showed I had performed the rite of passage. Elsewhere everywhere the hassle continued: tourists trying to ignore buzzing clouds of beggars, ragged young mothers lugging snot-nosed babes past not-nosed lepers and amputated old soldiers; fit young street-barbers who would stick a cotton-bud in your ear and start cleaning uninvited as you sat reading a newspaper, masseurs who seized your arm in a massage grip and fought you for possession as you walked along, all wanting the small pieces of grubby paper that pass for money. After as much as they could bear of their ignoring being ignored the targeted tourist might get angry and start shouting but it made no difference. They might call a policeman dozing in the shade of his booth who might then lay about the beggars with steel-tipped lathi for a few moments before going back to indifference leaving the tide of need to swirl around islands of travelling rich.

The travel-guides say don't give anything, you'll never get rid of them, you will be pestered in perpetuity but it was clear that this was happening anyway and, I thought, the tourists spend so much energy on refusal and get so upset, there must be a better way. I could not imagine going home and saying, as I had heard others, what a fantastic place India was, but for the beggars. I love to share, and always had Shantiji shouting quietly in my ear. Carrying one pocketful of 'small money', I could give a rupee or two, or a generous five, to whoever asked and I got back gratitude, jokes and laughter. It felt so good, being myself, walking my talk.

Back from the journey of enlightenment and in a new relationship I was keen to help my new family find the way of truth. Adopted parent of a ready-made child I discovered learning-by-mistake in the funfair season.

Beginning with small things, such as weaning our five-year-old off her addiction to ice cream by forbidding her to ask for it. (I can hear the guffaws of parents reading this.) Well, I was tired of the hassle, wasn't I? I had devoted years of energy and changed my life-style to eliminate stress and now here I was leading through the stalls of temptation a tearful little girl who instead of asking for ice-cream begged to be allowed to ask. How long before the 99-flake resumed its role as currency?

A lesson in tolerance and understanding, maybe, but a lesson in diagnosis for sure. She had always been given sweets or ice-cream for 'being good.' Her good was smiling sweetly, acting cute, quiet and obedient. Is that not perfect behaviour? She grew up, went to school, got good reports. I would read them and wonder if any child got high marks for expressing individuality or showing feelings. Grown-ups pay a therapist or find a fierce-eyed guru shouting 'Be Yourself' to help recover from the lifetime of pleasing and copying: of impression-management.

Sitting on your mat, focused on Treatment, the new client will be acutely aware of the impression they want to give. By subtly reflecting their movements and manner you begin to understand them. Offer tea, watch how they accept or decline, how they take the cup, how they drink. And how they look at you because they are, consciously or not, summing you up too!

What would be their diagnosis of you? What appearance do you present? And what impression are you giving? How are you sitting? Are you smiling or serious, welcoming or detached, warm or impersonal? Sitting the same way as the client sets them at ease. How? Why? Because you are copying and thereby pleasing. Is it not the sincerest form of flattery?

Be aware of space between and around you: not too close for comfort, not too detached. What kind of surroundings have they come into for their treatment? What sounds can they hear? What does your voice sound like? What odours or fragrances are in the air? What do you smell of? Are you efficient and professional or warm and friendly? Both?

Can they see the door, or have you seated yourself between them and the door? Is this important? It is to hippos – setting yourself between them and the river they see as cutting off their escape. They become dangerous. Ah, but you don't have any hippo clients? Would you therefore exclude from your learning-experience the primeval urges of creatures that have no interest in impression-management? Or do they? Those mighty toothsome yawns certainly give an impression. Can we learn from nature? From peacocks to lions to chameleons, nature's response to the primeval urges is impression-management. Where do you think we got it in the first place, we masters of illusion? Spielberg?

Looking diagnosis cuts both ways. You and your Receiver are together on your mat for the same reason: you both want satisfaction. At Spirit level your Receiver has chosen you as the right Giver for this moment. You have entered into a relationship of mutual healing that begins here with mutual diagnosis. In Nourishing Destiny, Lonny Jarratt suggests we diagnose not our Receiver so much as our relationship with them, the connection of our spirits. If you, say, are a Fire person, then another Fire person might not seem so hot to you whereas if they were Water you might boil them over – or they might put you out! Whatever the outcome, everything is perfectly right, a learning-experience in this lifetime.

Asking and Looking forms of diagnosis run along together. Look at your partner's eyes when you ask a question and see where they go. Your question enters the ears which turn the vibrations of your voice into the electronic bleeps that brain can understand as it goes searching among its many fibres. When Brain finds the information Mind selects a response for Brain to bleep-code and send to the tongue. Body is already replying in its own language and completely giving the game way.

Your question may have been of a factual nature, such as 'What kind of food do you eat?' Simple enough, straightforward answer, yes? Brain, directed by Mind, goes to the foodlist and Tongue recites. Or is your respondent on a diet and are they breaking that diet and are they concealing this fact from you for fear of your disapproval, you their perfect shiatsu person, or perhaps not yet arrived at that trust when they feel safe to show weakness? I remember my macrobiotic days – couldn't pass a sweetshop such were my cravings but would censor that information under questioning practice from fellow-students.

It might not be diet. It might be sexual, family or relationship problems they don't want to air: please, therapist, just get rid of the stomach tension, never mind the questions. While that thought lurks for some, others like to tell all in all its detail. How are they to know what you need to know? It is for you to hold the energy, and that fine line between diagnosis and gossip.

When Mind reframes what Brain found, the eyes wander to their right whereas if simply relaying the raw material of fact or experience they look more to their left. Right is fantasy, left is memory. Listening to the words they speak, being aware that they hear with their ears and answer with their eyes, trusting your own intuition and conscious of your compassion, you will find the right questions to let the layers unfold, to disclose the golden key that unlocks the door to their own well of self-healing. You can do so much on the mat. The rest is for them.

I like to practise my eye-diagnosis watching politicians on TV. I discover that not all of them lie all of the time. And switching off the sound is good practice observing body language.

You might find a few clients with opposite responses, which you can easily test with two questions, one fact/memory/experience, one fantasy/imagination/creativity, watching the eyes on the answers. Simple questions avoid too many thought-processes in the response.

For example: "Where do you live?" Fact.

"Do you imagine you will always live there?" Fantasy, reinforced by suggesting they use imagination to answer.

Easing into the asking diagnosis I explain the idea of Shiatsu and get permission to ask questions:

"Shiatsu works at different levels of body, mind, spirit. Sometimes it's an instant fix; sometimes the treatment needs to be spread over a few sessions. Let's see how this one goes and then work out a treatment plan to suit ...for now, may I ask a few questions, help me build up a picture of you as a whole being?"

By telling them they are a whole being I have sent a message to the subconscious. They might not yet know about their own power to self-heal, to make whole. Its not encouraged in a world dominated by drug-vendors both corporate and chaotic.

Besides which, people do sometimes let themselves get into such a state they stop believing themselves capable of anything. One client had decided she was a thoroughly bad person because she had neglected her son, deserted her husband and alienated her whole family when she was a heroin addict some fifteen years before. When she told me this she spoke as if in a trance, eyes left in memories brought into the present

"And now?" I asked.

"Well, I stopped using ten years ago."

"Do you see your son?"

"Yes, we get along fine nowadays but I worry about him because of what I did."

"How is he?"

"Well he's really healthy actually. And seems happy. And has a job he likes and a lovely girlfriend. We get on really well."

"What about your ex?"

"We've become friends. He doesn't hold grudges."

"Brothers? Sisters?"

"We've had our problems in the past but things are better now."

"So tell me again, why, specifically, do you think you are a thoroughly bad person?"

It was a habit she had formed, thinking about herself in that way. It wasn't rocket science to see it, not even therapy to help her see, just commonsense, how she had wrapped herself in outdated thoughts. She would never have worn outdated fashion.

In ten to fifteen minutes I have filled out my first impression, looking, listening, prompting. Questions bring awareness to areas of potential self-healing. If you ask about diet and the response is "Junk food, and too much of it!" what need is there to labour the point? Job done.

I ask about likes and dislikes, what makes you happy, what kind of thing upsets you. Questions about family reveal concerns about genetic conditions and childhood difficulties. However, "What is your relationship with your mother?" is not my favourite approach. Better, "Are both your parents alive?"

leading to, "and how is their health?"

and, "how do you get on with them?"

Sensitivity in touch follows sensitivity in talk.

Asking about diet, digestion and energy levels leads naturally down the body to issues of sexual energy and relationship. A picture forms of the internal and external environments hosting the stated conditions, with clues to the unstated and underlying causes.

How do you express yourself? What are the signs of spirit, of the predominant element of your natural constitution, showing through the conditioning of life? The leads lie in the language. Do you use expressions such as

"I see what you mean." Visual, possibly to do with Wood/Liver? or

"I hear what you're saying..." Auditory, tending towards Water/Kidney?

"I feel I understand..." Kinesthetic, perhaps indicating Earth/Spleen?

"I smelt a rat…" Olfactory: maybe Metal?

"It left a nasty taste in my mouth..." Taste, tongue-fire? or would you argue earth-spleen?

Where would you put "I see what you're saying?" or "I know where you're going?"

By responding to your client in similar language puts you, for the time being, in their world. As you see/hear/feel from their point of view you build their confidence that you understand them and begin to influence them towards self-healing.

Check your Asking and Looking by Sensing and Touching. Sensing or scanning the energy-field is to feel the different energy-levels, which may manifest as heat or cold, or a feeling of magnetic connection, or, just a feeling.

Touching Diagnosis is trusting Intuition to take your hands where needed, to harmonise imbalances of:

Kyo – the World of Need, emptiness, lack: often the underlying cause, a more Yin state.

Jitsu – more excessive; more obvious, often the symptom, and more Yang.

Sensing and Touching show what is going on in the present, the moment of treatment:

Diagnosis is treatment, treatment is diagnosis. Adapting to a Receiver's response to treatment combines your skill, compassion and intuition in a Zen paradox of Mu-Shin and mindfulness.

Treatment works on three levels:

Physical: the Japanese word shiatsu means finger-push. When your hand, finger or thumb contacts the skin of the Receiver, through the light clothing recommended for receiving a treatment, heat is generated, melting the gel around cells in the vicinity. As the gel becomes a solution, suspended toxins are released into the lymphatic system to be eliminated through the cardiovascular and respiratory systems. The endocrine system releases endorphins, natural healers.

Energetic: the solution allows conduction of the bioelectromagnetic Qi's healing message through the connective tissues and organ-meridian networks regulating the body-mind systems. The autonomic nervous system relaxes into freedom from tension.

Spiritual: Mu-Shin, Connection with Spirit and mindful Intuition lead to Intention: where the Mind goes, the Qi follows, and where the Qi flows, the blood follows. Your Intention is to help, to harmonise, and to allow, with love and compassion, without judgement.

Symptoms are outward signs of inward dis-harmony. Seek the deficiency, which allowed those symptoms develop. The treatment tonifies the kyo and disperses jitsu.

Let the love and compassion of the Heart Spirit infuse your Intention; be mindful of the healing power of Earth.

Becoming conscious of the Spirit connection between mind and body helps you in harmonising Qi flow in your client; meditational exercises such as Qi Gong and Tai Chi, your way of living, and attention to diet harmonise the flow in your Self.

As in conventional education you develop Skill and Knowledge. In Shiatsu training you also develop Intuition.

Self-cultivation and spiritual development enables you to avoid energy-depletion, contamination, and karmic debt: whether a Receiver suffers from a terminal condition, emotional problem, or simply needs stress relief, you guard against the risk of karmic interference by acknowledging, from a deep well of loving-kindness, that each being is responsible for itself.

"Let the right outcome happen"...without attachment to cure, or success.

Recommendations

It is remarkable how often, given a few suggestions, healing takes place long after the receiver has left the shiatsu mat. Assessing the interplay of Spirit-elements in the Receiver yields recommendations for self-healing and to prevent recurrence. Chi Self-massage, a little exercise, a few moments of meditation can often help a client transform stress into vitality. Not that they always follow. A doctor friend told me "They'll take the medicine but not the advice." Treat the participants' response to your recommendations as a useful diagnostic tools.

"D'you suppose," a student once said with dawning light, "that our participants have the same kind of difficulties with recommendations as we seem to have with homework?

Contra-indications and Controversy

Few conditions are absolutely forbidden treatment.

Cancer
There are two opposing views shiatsu treatment for cancer with medical evidence for neither. One is that enhancing energy-flow facilitates the spread of cancerous cells. The other claims by fortifying the immune system shiatsu helps counter the side effects of conventional medical treatment.

In reality, when a cancer patient seeks out a shiatsu practitioner they have usually sought elsewhere without satisfaction. It is for you to decide whether to treat them.

Children

Shiatsu being "Complementary" and not "Primary" health-care it is both contra-indicated and illegal to treat a sick child instead of referring it to a doctor for medical treatment. A signed disclaimer or authority from the parent does not legalise it!

Infectious/contagious diseases

Treatment is contra-indicated.

Pregnancy

In the first trimester pressure is contra-indicated on certain Tsubos with elimination properties.

Inflammation

Rotations, stretches and manipulations are contra-indicated.

You will become familiar with these matters, by absorption. When you start you want to learn everything today. Take it easy, take your time, it will come.

"He tires betimes who spurs too fast betimes...with eager feeding food doth choke the feeder..."

W. SHAKESPEARE

For me, the greatest learning was to trust the Universe to smile when I am in need. I sat on my rucksack in the dust of Varanasi. All the lodges were full. I had no money for a hotel and anyway who would want to live in western comfort away from the bubbling stews of life and death? They say if you die there you get off the wheel: as your body burns, at the moment your skull pops Lord Shiva whispers in your ear the mantra of salvation, releasing your soul from the burden of reincarnation. They come from far and wide to die in Varanasi. In the hostels for the dying occupancy is limited to a fortnight: then you must move out.

Opposite the burning ghats float barges filled with firewood from the south. Local forests have been erased to fuel fires that have consumed the dead for thirteen hundred years. Sometimes a penniless family can be seen on the far bank trying to burn a dead relative with insufficient sticks, leaving a partly consumed body for the fish.

Burning is purification by fire, the only exceptions being pregnant women whose karma is cleansed by the child within, saddhus who have cleansed their karma in this life and whose bodies are thrown sitting upright into the Ganges, and people who have died from the bite of a cobra, Shiva's sacred creature.

I knew none of this, sitting in the dust, until the universe smiled at me to follow three orange-clad saddhus through smelly backstreets to Shiva-Ganga Lodge, bare cells around small beautiful courtyard, a former monastery become a haven for wanderers lost in Shiva's sacred city.

She smiles as you ponder the meridians in shiatsu theory. Kneeling in position, book firmly closed or perhaps left in rucksack, think of the spirit of the meridian: the spirit of Fire, or Water, Earth, Metal or Wood.

Let your hand sense the air around your fellow-student or volunteer receiver: feel what you feel, in the emptiness of your palm.

See what you see, "look no hands" letting your eyes scan the subtle flow.

Nothing?

Then trust her ... and guess. Trace a line with your finger, anywhere, light and fast, no thought, Mu-Shin.

Don't be afraid to be wrong: it is a superior learning-experience, and Confusion a Virtue.

Then go to the book, look it up, and see how close you were. Try it!

Acknowledging the result without Praise or Blame allows you to step out of safety into the world of the new mind, like a two-year-old with neither knowledge nor experience, for whom every moment is an adventure in magic.

Study the child to learn True Spirit.

*   *   *

* Reinstall Innocence

* Love yourself

* Trust your instinct

* Love your shiatsu participant, he or she receiving your loving-touch

The installation continues through the Seven Steps to Learning.

* The Beginner runs

* The Intermediate struggles

* The Advanced knows

* The Practitioner understands

* The Teacher offers

* The Master shares

* The Sage learns

The Learning Formula for each step is the same.

* Trust your Intuition

* Follow your hands

Chapter 5
Leaning with Love

Leaning with Love

Given practice, your physical body adopts the right structure, as easily as your energy body takes the right position, as naturally as your true spirit falls into Love, given practice.

Shiatsu is moving Zen, stillness in motion, like a gliding swan, feet paddling unseen below.

Prepare by standing still. I feel the earth beneath my feet, always there. An earthquake in Los Angeles reminded me how I take it for granted, the constant support of earth. The bed shaking as if by an angry giant woke me. I lay helpless, at the mercy of a force beyond control or comprehension. The universe shifts in that moment. In a flash of mental lightning I saw how pathetic are the wretched small fears I create for myself, compared with this real and present terror. There was nothing I could do and no hiding place. I stumbled out of bed to join my friends under the doorways, apparently a safer place to be. Next morning we learned a huge building had collapsed, crushing hundreds, and a split appeared along the street.

Since then I have appreciated the earth holding me up, supporting me, providing from her surface and depths all my earthly needs, from food I eat to clothes I wear, to the aeroplane that takes me on holiday: all come from the earth, each needing different degrees of human energy to convert to a form in which it becomes of use.

With my feet grounded on earth my mind soars to the stars, through the visible universe and beyond, to connect with the source, True Spirit. This moment of standing stillness settles me in my human place, between Heaven and Earth, drawing on both.

Hands light against my thighs, I bend my knees, lowering myself to the floor beside my receiver, until my sitting-bones rest on my heels.

Before our energy-fields blend I use the Cosmic Bubble to bring the Yang and Yin energies into harmony, setting my Qi to a different vibration, to avoid being affected by my receiver's condition.

Raise hands palm-up above head.

Looking up, connect with the spirit of Heaven: Yang energy, the night sky, the stars and planets, galaxies and constellations of the Visible Universe.

Stretch both arms out sideways and lower them palm-down to the floor.

Join hands in prayer-position on lap.

Looking downwards and inward, mentally connect with the spirit of Earth, Yin energy; feel the supporting earth beneath you and connect the central sun deep below with the spirit of the universe above and within.

Hold the position for a few moments, rooted in the Circle of Protection.

Focus on the receiver and silently affirm: "You are not my problem, I am not your solution. Let the right outcome happen."

Giving Shiatsu: The First Touch

The simple combination of Intention, Energy and Movement protects you on different levels:

* by containing your energy field,

* by opening the Yang-Yin channels,

* by letting go the ego's desire for success,

* by acknowledging your Receiver's contract with Heaven,

* by settling yourself into a rooted position from which you can flow harmoniously into treatment.

Positioning

Leaning into the floor position for shiatsu is really very easy, a memory of one of your very first learnings. If you are lucky enough to know a tiny friend relatively new to this world, one who still operates at floor level, pay them a visit and watch how they get about. Pick up a few tips on managing yourself in that small world: you lived there yourself once, before getting big and standing up lifted you into what at the time might have seemed a superior position. Notice the intense curiosity of a little person on discovery.

If you don't have an acquaintance in the under-one population crawl about the floor yourself for a while. Try it now: nobody's looking – are they? Keep your head up to see where you go, wiggle your back to check flexibility, and notice how easy it is to get about when you don't have to think of keeping upright. You have extra stability down there although you can't go quite so fast: this is no bad thing. Slowing down time is a special shiatsu skill: you can do so much more in a few minutes. (You can also learn to speed it up, very useful in the recovery process – and on long flights.)

See how easy it is to vary your palm-pressure with your weight. When you notice your wrists aching you may feel a sense of gratitude that you didn't take up, for instance, marathon running as a career, and reassure yourself that the ache will go away when you have had a little more practice and your wrists become more used to this new activity. Pay attention to your bodily response and take care not to do too much too soon. Many people can get carried away in their enthusiasm for this new profession of helping others.

Working on all fours is pleasurable (horses love it) and knowing it will come with practice takes off the pressure to get it right first time. This would be a good thing to remember in other aspects of learning. Over the years I have found a few handy tips that help me almost fall into place from sitting on my heels in the Cosmic Bubble:

Giving Shiatsu: Position 1

* Opening knees as wide apart as hips

* Kneeling up and bending forward from the waist

* Placing palms on Receiver's body, no farther apart than the width between knees

* With almost straight arms resting weight on hands

* Kneeling up, sink down

* Filling needy space

* Natural pressure

* Let the hungry kyo

* Feast on the jitsu!

From this position it feels natural to lean a little forward and a little back to alter the pressure of your hands. When leaning on your shiatsu client place hands for the first pressure on the two places best able to take the weight: left between the shoulder-blades, right hand on sacrum, these being also the two highest points of the body when prone and, incidentally, the farthest apart for hands to be. Any wider would risk misalignment and loss of 'the connection.'

Ask your Receiver, 'How's the pressure?'

If they reply OK then make sure with, 'Would you like a little more or a little less?' – just in case they think you know what's best for them. They know what's best: you want to help them realise it.

Natural, Leaning, Perpendicular pressure feels so good, both to give and to receive. By keeping one knee close to the body and moving the other a few inches back, your structure aligns in perfect asymmetry.

'Shiatsu Position Number 1' gives connection, stability and groundedness. To move around the body, adjust your structure to 'Shiatsu Position Number 2' by lifting one knee so that your sole is on the floor. You lose just a little pressure but gain more flexibility of direction. By changing from one knee to the other you can keep your hands perfectly still yet change direction by 90 degrees or so.

Connecting the flow of Qi, Giver directs her own Hara to Receiver. With both Position 1 and 2, Giver feels only one place of contact between her hands and so it feels to the Receiver. As above, so below: the Connection has been made and as you move around the body and move the body around that connection is easily sustained using both structures, flowing one into the other according to your changing movements.

It is in the stillness that you feel the connection: each hand growing warm as the warmth radiates, both hands connected by this bioelectromagnetic force-field, a pool of loving-kindness.

Giving Shiatsu: Position 2

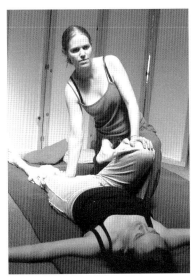

* Feeling in the Flow
* Let Other Hand join
* Mother Hand. Connect
* The flow between them
* Be aware, be there!

Take care to avoid

* Twisting hara out of alignment
* Blocking hara with knee
* Over-extension: hands further apart than hips, or reaching out too far
* Knees too open, which would disperse qi, or too closed which would render structure unstable
* Mechanical/rhythmical movement

By moving just one hand at a time you keep that connection throughout the treatment. The still hand anchors as you change position, the other moving on. Settle again into natural, leaning perpendicular pressure in the new position while your Receiver has been anchored in the stillness of the Motherhand.

Practise leaning on your Receiver, leaning with love, as trusting as your tiny friend leans on mother earth for support. Moving is easy and natural, and time slows down.

The truth is, in shiatsu as in life, so often what looks good feels good and as your pace slows to match the deepening relaxation of your Receiver you unconsciously adopt an attitude of unpredictable elegance as you follow your hands around the territory, lingering in places of instinct attraction.

As a beginner I found the most challenging aspect of giving shiatsu was the physical movement and arranging the structure of my own body while going around the mat, around the person I was treating in whatever position. It was a true gift of spirit that showed me a way to solve this. In learning Tai Chi I had developed 'Spirit-Vision', watching my teacher go through the graceful movements of the form. He told us to watch him and then to imagine that we could see our spirits moving with him, copying his movements and then visualising joining our spirit as if stepping into it with our physical body and following its moves. Later in 'push-hands', we learned to 'see' the spirit of the opponent and sense their intention.

Tai Chi is a martial art and Shiatsu the art of gentle healing but both use the same energy applied in different ways and what I learned about upright movement in Tai Chi I found of great help in the floor-level movements of shiatsu. When ready to move I use spirit-vision to see myself in the new place. With that picture in mind I imagine I can look down on myself and see how I get there, where to place my hands and how to move my legs. My physical body flows into the new structure. It became easy and felt so natural as long as I held my focus.

Giving Shiatsu: Seated Position

In seated you can reach both back and front at the same time, all around head, neck and shoulders, and can test the full range of arm movement.

Let my hand alight

Like a resting breath

On the place of need

Let me understand

Like a wise mother

Later, learning how to treat different conditions I found spirit-vision enabled me to see into the participant's energy-field: my hands would go to the right meridian or point. But in the early stages it was the trick of picturing myself moving and following the pictures that helped me develop the confidence that led to grace of movement.

Confidence and grace increase with practice as you play on different sizes and shapes of people, turning them from prone to side to supine to seated, each position needing a different degree of sensitivity.

The **back** is stronger and can take more pressure prone; give the same in seated and your participant topples.

In **seated** you can reach both back and front at the same time, all around head, neck and shoulders, and can test the full range of arm movement.

Prone and **supine** enable natural, leaning, perpendicular pressure to meridians and points of the arms. Testing leg movement is more effective in supine.

Side position is wonderful for relaxation (most of us sleep this way) and for participants less able to lie prone.

Each position naturally presents a different set of meridians.

Watching my participant respond to treatment in any position tells me when they want to change: after lying face down for a while they may turn their head the other way. This is a good time to turn them over. Lying supine leads to a slight flexion in the lower back: a good move would be into side.

Practise yourself to find out how long you can comfortably lie face down; how long flat on your back with your outstretched legs; how long seated in one position before your body tells you it wants to move; and for how long you can lie still on your side. Notice when

Giving Shiatsu: Side Position

Side position is wonderful for relaxation (most of us sleep this way) and for participants less able to lie prone.

you begin to fidget: head, limb or body movements. Notice what you do; notice what your Receivers do.

As your training continues you develop a profound and lasting sensitivity to the physical response of those who entrust you with themselves for treatment. If they get up off the mat at the end rubbing their neck or back I might just ask them to lie down again! Or make a mental note to pay more attention.

I talk to my Receiver as I go about the treatment. Communicating at the mundane level helps connection in the energy and spirit dimensions. My talk may seem random but is interspersed with questions and suggestions. Asking diagnosis starts things off before they even lie down and eases them into responding – if I have said nothing for the first twenty minutes and then suddenly talk, it shakes them out of the shiatsu trance with a startled grunt. The trance can be sustained by soft conversational murmurs, asking about the pressure when you lean in a new place, for example, or filling in any carefully left gaps from asking diagnosis. I do make a point of reassuring them before I start, "I might ask you more questions during the treatment, which does not mean I have found something untoward, just filling in anything I might have forgotten to ask before."

This encourages ongoing feedback but be careful: people sometimes think the worst. Telling your Receiver their "Kidney energy is low," can be taken to imply a problem with the kidney organs, and then you are faced with explaining the theory of Chinese medicine to a worried client who has suddenly lost all sense of relaxation. A farmer friend in my training days really got the wind up when I suggested he have his heart checked out next time he went for his routine medical.

I knew his diet included excessive amounts of cheese, other dairy, and salami. His face had a reddish hue, with indentations at the tip of his bulbous nose and in both earlobes. When I put pressure on points around the heart area he said it hurt. Following the shiatsu he got into his car, drove to A&E and said he was going to have a heart attack.

The doctor asked if he had had any knocks lately. Yes, he had been butted by one of his cattle. The diagnosis? A hairline fracture of the rib was causing the chest pain.

Had I been wrong? I thought so at the time and my confidence was shaken. I gave up making suggestions. Self-doubt flourished like brambles. One year later my farmer was stretchered off an aeroplane after an emergency landing in Australia. He had a heart attack.

I am still careful of what I say. Our clients invest in us a kind of authority and I believe we ought to cultivate a special awareness of the effects of our words. One of my students was told – by her reflex-ologist! – that she was suffering the effects of past-life wrong-doing. She came away feeling helpless. Is it really necessary to show people how clever, insightful and enlightened we healers are – and without fear of contradiction?

We have no power to change the past but we can change the light in which we view past events, whether in this life or another. What about someone else's view of your past lives? Can you check it out, or must you take as gospel what they see, say and interpret?

Some years ago I went to a shamanic healer for help in letting go the ties to a former partner with whom I had done sex-magickal bonding. Drummed into trance I saw visions of a past life. Later the practi-tioner handed me pen and paper to write down all I had seen, and did the same herself. Our accounts were not identical but similar enough to convince me the experience of life in the past lane was valid. She made no suggestions, imposed no "inside knowledge", claimed no psychic powers and simply helped me see myself.

Rather than using our powers of suggestion to condition a patient into believing they are powerless to change we could consider convincing them of the converse. Simple use of language can help. When a client says they are suffering from this or that illness, ask, "Are you suffer-ing? Do you see yourself as one who suffers, a sufferer?" You sow a seed of realisation that to see oneself as a victim is to fertilise an envi-ronment that allows conditions to take root, grow and flourish.

Power of suggestion can be used for the good, combining Talk and Touch to anchor positive feelings in the organ-meridian networks. Healing vibrates throughout the energy-field long after your participant has left the mat. You will know their need from the asking and looking diagnoses or, if none are obvious, trust intuition.

For someone whose life seems lacking in love or joy, suggest - in a conversational rather than "therapist" tone of voice – they think of a time, a moment even, when they felt happy, joyful, loved or loving: any moment in their life. Later, during the treatment when they are lying supine, place your hand on their heart and ask them to remember that moment. Ask them to remember what they saw, heard and felt while your Motherhand anchors that good feeling in the organ-meridian network of the Heart, embedding that good feeling in the cellular, energetic and spiritual body. Heart is the Monarch, the Sovereign Organ in shiatsu, ruling the emotions of love and joy.

My very first practice-client told me straight out there was no joy in his life. A heavy-set, serious man, he worked in a bank and practised meditation in his free time, gave and went to dinner parties and made a lot of money. Single, in his forties, he wore dark banking suits and moved with deliberation. I had only just started learning shiatsu and not yet studied the interactions of organs and emotions. Nor had I got to the place of asking Intuition for an answer - but the point of Intuition is to answer before being asked and I heard myself saying, "What do you do for fun, Robert?"

I could see his mind analysing his leisure activities: evenings, weekends and holidays. "Not a lot," he said.

"Very well," said my voice, "my prescription for you is to learn salsa."

Where did that come from? It could not have worked better. He met and fell in love with a Brazilian girl. I danced at their uproariously joyful wedding and am ungodfather to the first of their three children. Now I visit him in his bustling home filled with joy and kids' laughter. His face has got used to smiling.

A subtle approach to problems is effective in shiatsu where Touch is part of the job, the part that attracts people to our therapy. What I mean by subtle is planting the seeds early and watering the flowers later. Elicit the basic need, say, "lack of love", in the asking diagnosis, without offering an instant solution. Find out where and when the person has experienced love in the past: love for anyone or anything, anything that makes a good feeling.

With this information you go into the treatment and, when your Receiver is in a position for you to connect with the related organ, remind them of the good feeling and reinforce it, physically connecting with the Motherhand. Afterwards you might make suggestions or recommendations of specific practical ways in which they can fill the need themselves.

A basic need might be in areas other than emotion, but traceable back to that source. Lack of assertiveness, for instance, could arise from a deficiency in courage, to do with the lung meridian and the metal element. The spirit of metal can cut and contain, reflect and inspire. If a client felt they ought to be more assertive I would ask them to recall a time when they had stood up for themselves, even if only in a small way, and remember everything about that moment, what they saw, heard, said, did and felt. The lung points, where the meridian starts in front of the shoulders, are perfect spots for Motherhand to anchor the feeling of courage.

What would you do for indecision? How might you help your client reinstall decisiveness, what do you think is the related organ-meridian network, what treatment-position would be appropriate for anchoring the good feeling, and in which location or point?

Sometimes it's not a deficiency that needs attention so much as excess. Anger, greed, sadness, jealousy – you can think of many more of those emotions or feelings which make life bumpy but everyone has the resources at some level to cope and while they are relaxing in shiatsu we can help them access those resources and anchor the good feelings in the meridians, using the structural down-flowing Yang meridians to clear the energy-field and the supporting upward-flowing Yin meridians to draw healing energy up from the Earth.

Every side has another side: for every excess there is a compensating deficiency. In our shiatsu we can help others into balance. But what of us, the Givers?

It makes sense, does it not, to look after yourself in order to look after someone else? In airline videos and safety demonstrations they tell us to put on our own oxygen mask before putting one on our child.

Offering healing to others we sometimes risk depletion or contamination of our own energy, or vulnerability to karmic debt. Protection from energy depletion or contamination starts with life-style. The Cosmic Bubble works for individual treatments but, when giving a lot of shiatsu especially to people with medical/emotional conditions, protection becomes part of your way of being.

I like to spend a little time every day in meditation and exercise, a little care noticing what I eat, and a lot of care about environments and situations I put myself into, who I hang out with, even the kind of movies I watch.

Sarita, a non-smoking teetotal vegetarian, whom I worked with in my clinical training, practised meditation and yoga and, living in the city, made sure to spend time in nature. Yet every so often she turned up at the clinic exhausted, restless, jumpy, energy jagged, unable to give shiatsu until she had received a treatment herself.

"What's the story?"

"The usual. Kidney abuse: I watched a horror movie last night. Why do I do it?"

I find it helpful to observe myself, reactions and responses to situations, their effect on my wellbeing. Simply observing to start with, not making changes. Writing down what you do and noting how you feel gives awareness and informed choice: to do something, or do nothing; to change or stay the same. I certainly had some interesting insights when I began this self-observation: feelings of guilt about diet or habits were not helpful, but I realised what was going on. And understood myself better.

Our new-age p.c. society is never short of advice on diet, exercise, life-style, meditation. In fact I frequently find myself giving it. But is what's good for me right for you?

During a long trip to the United States I could afford either to travel around by 'Thanks for going Greyhound' bus or to stay in one place. I chose travel, visiting some 40 states all of which seemed to be carnivorous, from the roadside diners of Route 66 to the 99-cent 24-hour casino breakfasts of Las Vegas. My hitherto macrobiotic diet was forgotten across the Atlantic.

Back in London, I filled my basket at Clearspring Healthfoods with miso soup and aduki beans, tofu and sea vegetables, organic produce and short-grain brown rice. Then the girl at the checkout spoke one of those throwaway life-changing lines, "A happy man can eat what he likes!"

Pause for silent thunder.

Was I a happy man? Did I like what I had bought to eat? Well, yes, well, but! But what? But I found it hard – no, let's rephrase – I found it impossible to pass a sweet-shop without buying sweets, ice-cream, chocolate. Why? Oh, such a very good reason: the comforting words of Cam, my macrobiotic teacher, "Each day you should eat something bad for you. Keeps the organs functioning." Macrobiotics went along very well with practising shiatsu, my main job, and made me feel at home among other practitioners, students, teachers and fellow-travellers on the path to ensomethingment.

Reflecting, in the passing of millionths of nanoseconds, I realised I was using my diet as a kind of passport to acceptance by my peers, paying lip-service without lip-licking, except when indulging in the salty, sweet, fatty and illicit luxuries of my hunter-gatherer ancestors. I had so loved my eating abroad!

With a brief insincere apology I restocked their shelves and went down Victor's caff in Whitecross Street market for bacon and eggs, toast and marmalade, hot strong tea with milk and sugar.

Over the weeks that followed I reverted to the diet of my upbringing: meat and potatos, lovely fresh veg, and discovered that eating what I like can keep me happy and healthy too, because if I take a huge meal early in the day then not only do I not need to eat again – maybe a piece of toast or some soup the evening – but also lost, immediately, the cravings for sweets and ice-cream that had plagued my macrobiotic years.

I still take care: with a long-term dodgy gallbladder too much of certain foods makes me uncomfortable, or ill: but listening to my body I made friends with it, so I compromise and eat what we both like. In this way my food is reinstated as a source of energy, instead of using energy up in the struggle to keep to someone else's idea of 'the right diet.'

Energy is the fuel of the shiatsuka; the giver of shiatsu, and much of your training is to do with its conservation. Spending time with yourself before and after treatments reduces the risk of depletion or contamination.

A Receiver's condition however serious, from hangover to terminal, affects their energy field and can influence yours – if you let it. Here they are, feeling a bit rough, drained, wiped out even. Along comes their bright shiny shiatsuka, glowing with vitality: the celestial suction-pump kicks in. By the end of the treatment all that yummy Qi has been sucked into the Receiver, leaving the Giver completely, well, given.

You must know at least one person who has a similar effect on you even if you're not giving them shiatsu. They could be a natural energy-parasite. You might tend to avoid them in your day-to-day existence, but what if such a person lands on your mat wanting treatment?

Reaffirming responsibility as a routine reminder reinforces immunity from depletion.

Jane has come to Jim for treatment. Jim kneels beside her lying on the mat. He looks into his heart, into the deep well of loving-kindness and, from that place of love, silently affirms:

"Jane is not my problem. I am not her solution."

For a few moments he reflects on her situation. She may be suffering from a serious condition or simply need stress relief, or comfort. It is not for Jim to interfere with her karma and he acknowledges this with a silent prayer:

"Let the right outcome happen."

What is the right outcome? Different for each individual, it begins even before we are born. At the moment of conception each one of us enters into a "Contract with Heaven" and everything that happens to us in this life is part of that contract, a gift of heaven.

Our reaction or response to situations affects our Contract, our acceptance, rejection or simple acknowledgement of the Gift. For example, stuck in a traffic jam, we must wait. We can't disappear the traffic. We can choose to wait with patience, using the time as Gift from Heaven, to call clients or reconnect with friends and family, listen to the radio or Ipod, or meditate. Or we can wait with impatience, anger and frustration, generating toxic stress.

Toxic stress is the source of most conditions. While stress itself is necessary for our nervous system to function and our muscles to develop, toxic stress makes us ill. If we look upon every situation as a gift, blessing or learning-experience, this life can become a source of joy.

The shiatsu receiver lying on our mat, waiting for the loving-touch of your hands, is living in their life at this moment. They have lived from the moment of conception. Who knows how they have lived with their contract from Heaven, how much they have varied it, what toxic stress they hold? Who knows what went before, and what their soul brought into this life?

Who knows what is the right outcome? Sometimes the soul wants to go. Who are we to decide?

My father died peacefully after nearly ninety years. At his funeral my mother said, "He always goes ahead. He makes sure everything's safe, then he sends for me."

They had travelled all their lives, in Europe, South America and Africa.

A week later she was in hospital. Eighty years old, she had experienced heart disease, kidney problems and arthritis. They put her in Intensive Care and rigged her up to a battery of machines. Features collapsed, she lay as if in a space-ship, lights and screens faintly winking and humming around her. The nurse, dynamic in Reeboks and grey tracksuit, reassured me:

"We're really going to fight for this old lady!"

After three days of mechanically sustained life my mum opened her eyes. "I don't want this any more," she whispered. "I'm ready. I don't want to stay behind now."

The hospital respected her wish and let her go with the flick of a switch and as she left, the smile returned. She shares the same earth with her husband of fifty years and their headstone reads: Journeying on Together.

Deep within we have a well of healing, for ourself, for others. If you, a shiatsuka, can help your receiver to be aware of that deep well, you have done your job. It is for them to draw from their well, or to leave it.

We are, most of us, born healthy and we are, most of us, fundamentally healthy throughout much of our lives. Our natural state is of health. Health is our Nature, and the work of the shiatsuka is to act as a kind of go-between, between our natural state and the temporary conditions affecting our natural state.

How can you discern their natural state? You will have spoken to your client to make the appointment. Or did they have someone else ring up for them? This is useful and interesting information. If they made their own appointment you will have heard their voice. What did they sound like?

Would you accept an appointment for someone who did not make it himself, or herself?

Or would you make a judgement that they were too busy to see to their own health?

Or did a well-meaning concerned partner make the appointment?

Has the day or time of the appointment been changed? Often?

My goodness, how you can learn about someone before they even turn up!

"Emptiness is in fact form when we forget the self. There's nothing in the universe other than ourself. Nothing to compare, name, or identify. When it's the only thing there is, how can we talk about it?"

TAIZAN MAEZUMI

Sit, still in body and mind, listening in silence, open to any impressions that may come, or none.

Kneeling, tune in to your Receiver's energy, looking as if through the physical body, looking to the imbalances: too much here, stuck there, empty elsewhere.

Such insight, scanning with spirit, precise, unexplainable, is already present in each of us, to greater or lesser degree: it works by allowing the possible, and improves with practice.

Now with a general impression of the energy being, look for local impressions: moving one hand over the back, close but without actually touching, sensing for energy-impressions with the your palm, relating this to the physical body, diagnostic areas, and energy-centres or chakras, or meridians and points. Your being absorbs the information.

Trust the receptive power of Instinct which, rarely if ever wrong, is better than not following it at all. And the more you do it, the more you will understand why. For now, let it be, and follow your hands.

Later, checking out what you did, relating to your Receiver's condition, you will find it was the treatment you would have given after painstaking analysis, the very nature of which is to second-guess…Martin Luther King called it the paralysis of analysis.

Is there a difference between analysis and diagnosis? You sit there chatting to your participant learning all about their life; they sit there enjoying your full attention while they chat away about themselves: is it any wonder shiatsu is so addictive? They go to the doctor who is so busy he's written the prescription before looking up, they go to the massage therapist who is not supposed to diagnose and just rubs their body, they go to their psycho-therapist who likes to hear them cry and is not supposed to rub their body at all and now here they are, sitting on your mat telling you their troubles and then getting a nice shiatsu massage.

Plus all the Yin and Yang stuff, little insights into the mystical world of oriental healing, talk of energy stuck or flowing, points in the foot to relieve pain in the neck, or on the shoulder for pain in the colon, how organs and meridians network and how the five elements (five?) feed or starve each other: a whole new world.

Yin and Yang is a simple concept. The words describe the relationship between things. Like a rain-drop and a tsunami for example. The rain-drop is more yin and the tsunami more yang. Both are water that is more yin than fire. What about a candle-flame and a forest blaze? Both are fire: the blaze would be more yang than the flame but in comparison with the sun, more yin. It gets rather more interesting when comparing different elements: which would you consider more yang, the flame or the rain-drop? What if all the drops joined forces and made a rainstorm? Which would be more yin, making the other more yang? The storm and the blazing forest? Play with it a little. You can relate more yang and more yin to people you know.

Yang was the bright side of the hill, in the light and warmth of the sun; yin, the other side, cooler, in the shade. And as the sun moves across the sky or the earth twirls on her axis, the light and warmth shift, illuminating the shade even while leaving other shadows behind. In the course of a day yang moves into and becomes yin, and yin becomes yang. This is life, is it not? The ups and downs, ins and outs, and how they affect you, or your client, depend on the perception. Rain might be good for the farm but bad for the picnic. It's the same rain.

As Yin and Yang describe the natural flows of life, Kyo and Jitsu describe the distortions that occur from time to time. Reminder:

> Kyo – the world of emptiness, neediness, lack: often the under lying cause of a condition

> Jitsu – more excessive; more obvious, often the symptom.

For example, with a cold the eyes are red, the nose runny and sneezing: excess activity in comparison with not having a cold. Less obvious is the deficiency in the immune system that let you catch it in the first place.

Kyo and Jitsu are measures of degrees of imbalance: a radiator, for example, keeps you warm by heating the room. I would not call this heat a jitsu condition: it is what the radiator does. However, if the radiator were broken therefore cold when it should be hot, I would certainly describe it as kyo. In summer, switched off and cool is a normal state for the radiator: no imbalance thus neither jitsu nor kyo.

What would you say about the air-conditioner?

In those early days of determination to 'fix' people it was always my aim to get rid of the jitsu so that they immediately felt better and went away full of admiration and gratitude. It takes only a little training and experience to realise the futility of that particular trip, a few treatments which don't work quite so well as one would have anticipated leaving the wretched ego fluctuating between beating itself up and blaming the receiver. You soon get over it.

I know that to start with you want each treatment to show a result, and a better result than the one before. What does it take to leave all that conditioning where it belongs and just get on with giving shiatsu without thought of personal gratification? Go to the root of your own motivation - why are you doing this:

To give a good treatment

Why?

To help the recipient

Why?

To make them feel better

Why?

Etc

Rigorous self-examination about motive avoids ego-tripping and interference with karma. Are you doing it for the thanks, the joy in their eyes, the pleasant feeling you get yourself?

Please understand, this is not to condemn any motive but to recognise it. Honour your ego: it keeps you alive. A strong ego is self-reliant and positive. A weak ego needs constant feeding. The equation of ego with negativity springs from a flawed doctrine, distorted from its root.

Without joining the ego-beaters (not singling out any particular belief-system) it only takes a simple, practical approach to treatment without attachment to result: just do it!

First see to the deficiency, the kyo. Think for a moment about the rich and the poor. The rich have a lot, the poor not. The rich invest energy in keeping what they have and so are difficult to rob: one would come up against guards and Rottweilers, security fences and attitude. I don't think it would be stretching it too far to describe rich as a jitsu condition, one of excess. Some are willing to share, a little. And some have been known, when attacked by authority, first to resist and then to disappear into hiding.

The poor are different. I have found in my travels a culture of sharing, among those who seem to have the least. Often willing to give, but perhaps not always so willing to receive when a little pride gets in the way.

Relating this to a kyo jitsu imbalance, it makes sense to me to work on the kyo first: you soon notice how this approach lets the kyo replenish itself by drawing from the jitsu, restoring the harmony intended by Nature. And you, rather than getting into a fight by attacking the jitsu, the symptom, have fulfilled your role as intermediary between the spirit of the receiver and its natural state of wellness by helping it access that deep well of self-healing power lying within each one of us.

Treatments lasting under an hour avoid depletion of Giver and Receiver both. The First Touch is the Last and Giver takes time to disconnect gently, as if saying goodbye to a friend. Afterwards, reflect on what you found: ask your receiver what they felt: precious information that helps with your approach next time. Personally, I find the question "How do you feel now?" often elicits an answer about how nice the treatment felt. "What do you feel now?" yields a more useful response.

Healing processes may be spread over a series of treatments: its not a good idea to detoxify in one session more than the body can eliminate – the healing crisis can be too severe. Ohashi says a healing crisis is often the result of the therapist's eagerness (ego-ness?) to get a result.

Time and Money

Time and Money matter for even the most chilled-out, laid-back and altruistic of givers. Once these two little demons are contained in their rightful place, neither worshipped nor denied but treated with appropriate respect, they become willing helpers.

How long should a treatment last? As long as it takes, say the wise old wizards, depending on the condition of the Receiver, the connection with the Giver, karmic influences and so on. Clients want more precise timings because of other things in life such as work, home, hairdressing appointments, parking meters, trains to catch/meet, kids to take/pick up from school or ballet/judo classes.

"How long, how many and how much" questions focus on the expectations, hopes and fears of your potential clients. How long should you spend on one treatment-session? And how many sessions in a day? An overlong treatment can deplete the Receiver, too many can deplete the Giver.

A graduate student announced she could give eight to ten treatments a day and feel "Fine," afterwards. And, she added, "I give my all, one hundred and ten percent."

The Taoist teacher Mantak Chia told her, "You work too hard, not enjoy enough. Give just two or three treatments a day, and 50% effort."

"But what if the patient needs more?"

"Then you have more to give! If you've already given 100%, what's left? And nothing for yourself."

"But what if I need more patients? I can't make my living from just two or three treatments a day."

Chinese shrug. "Charge more."

Fee doubled, appointments halved, life better!

My own formula is to tell potential clients their shiatsu could take "up to an hour." I start with ten to fifteen minutes listening, finding out how they've been since the previous session, how they are getting on with "homework" suggestions, and so on. Another half-hour or so hands-on leaves ten or fifteen minutes at the end for recommendations. Keep it flexible, though: vary to individual needs. And, for me, allowing half an hour between clients makes time to prepare: relax, meditate, read or write up notes.

Use their "How many treatments" question to explain that it varies from person to person. We have no standard people: although conditions may be similar it is the whole person receiving shiatsu. Occasionally just one treatment can help, more often between four and eight. You will have a clearer idea at the end of the first session, so suggest making a treatment plan based on that, and review it after four sessions.

Sometimes people are late; sometimes they don't turn up at all. And of course the fewer you are seeing, the bigger the impact on your finances! I am still owed money by a rock musician in Chelsea. It began with, "Mind if I pay you next time" and ended after some weeks with, "That's ridiculous – I never had that many sessions!" He was right, because I had included the three sessions when I had gone to his house at the appointed times and found him to be not there.

I let the debt go: the stress affected my general state of serenity and the learning-experience was worth more than the payment he owed. When someone books an appointment I tell them they must pay the full amount if they don't turn up, or if they cancel at less than 48 hours notice. I give or send them an appointment card or email, confirming time, day and place, and call them the day before.

With people who ask to pay next time, I often wonder if they made the same request at the petrol-station, or to the railway clerk who sold them their ticket to travel to the appointment. (Once somebody said, "No, I jumped the barrier to get here!")

Nowadays I ask "next timers" to send their payment before we book the next session, and then I forget about it. If the payment does arrive I will see them. If not, I have lost only one fee, and don't have the stress of worrying about next time.

Have you ever been late? Has someone ever been late for you? It happens, doesn't it. We with our busy lives…Sandy, shiatsu student, was habitually ten to fifteen minutes late for class, always with a raft of reasons. One Thursday afternoon she arrived early, face smudged with tears.

"What's up?"

"Bloody bank-managers. They're all inhuman and mine's a bastard." She had run up an overdraft, the bank had been asking for its money back, and now had given her an ultimatum.

I had always asked her why she was late. Now I said, "Why are you early for class today?"

She replied, "I realised what was going on in my life. I owe money all over the place and I'm late everywhere I go so I've been owing time too. I've just got to get myself together. So I decided to start by being on time for class. Up to now my whole life has relied on other people putting themselves out for me."

"Even the bank manager?"

She laughed then. "No, I guess he's just being a bank manager. Its what they do isn't it, lend money and get it back. I'd never really thought of the back part. Oh well, journey of a thousand miles…"

"…starts with a single step."

Sandy got a part-time job waitressing. After clearing her money-debts she concentrated on full-time shiatsu, with a mobile (visiting) practice and working in clinics. One day she called me. "What do you do about people who are always late for appointments?"

Full circle!

What do you do? What a wonderful learning-experience. Do we think our clients will never be late for a clinic appointment? An uncomfortable incident from the second year of my own training comes to mind: most of us drifted in around the 10.30 mark, some as late as 11. The subject was Time Management. The teacher set the scene:

"I am in my clinic, preparing for the first shiatsu of the day. The person is late. I begin to feel a little anxious, as it is their first time. After 20 minutes I begin to think, do they still expect an hour? How am I going to fit it all in? They arrive, flustered and apologetic. I hide my resentment.

"My second appointment was to have started a half-hour after my first ended. Now I have no time to write up notes on the first, prepare for the second, have a cup of tea, cleanse my energy-field or any of the things I need to do. If I give the full treatment, with asking-diagnosis, time to readjust, suggestions, recommendations and re-booking, I will run over time. My next person will be kept waiting. My room-booking will run over – I'll have to pay for more time for the room. And catch a later train and be late picking my kids up from school! Help!"

He had us discuss various responses to this stressful situation. Then he looked at those students who had arrived late for his class and said,

"How do you feel about this?"

Busted! We learned that time is a responsibility, punctuality the politeness not only of princes. What I wondered, were the qualities of a perfect practitioner? And how do we acquire these attributes of the True Spirit of a Zen Shiatsuka?

"Is it more virtuous to cultivate virtue, than simply to be virtuous?"

J. KRISHNAMURTI

---

*   *   *

The Perfect Shiatsuka!

Relaxed	Alert
Aware	Focused
Cool	Warm
Calm	Passionate
Sensitive	Direct
Still	Mobile
Meticulous	Intuitive
Precise	Inspired
Accepting	Inquisitive
Self-contained	Helpful
Gentle	Firm
Stable	Flexible
Grounded	Spiritual
Laid back	Intense
Loving	Detached
Hand of Mother	Mind of Samurai
Yin	Yang

Chapter 6
Spirits of the Being

Spirits of the Being

"Medicine" works on the body, "Healing" on the mind. At school, physical education and biology taught me something about my body, other studies a little about my mind. Learning shiatsu, half a lifetime later, I began to understand what connects the one to the other. Western medicine claims not to deal in spirit but any doctor will tell you that you can worry yourself sick. Can you laugh yourself better? Our therapy, developed in the rural communities and imperial courts of ancient China, still works today because it make sense. In Zen Shiatsu we acknowledge the heart connection of love and compassion as the essence of healing, based on the organ-meridian networks in their physical, mental and spiritual aspects.

Rivers flow through the countryside, irrigating fields. The meridians are the rivers, the organs the fields, the watering-holes the points. In a modern city the meridians are the streets, the points being the intersections and junctions, and the organs the utilities that maintain them. In the city there are peak times and slack times, and sometimes things break down. In the countryside the weather affects and shapes the living landscape.

Spring sees the green budding of new life in plants and trees that bear fruit in the red heat of summer. Ripe yellow fields lie ready to reap before grey autumn sets in. Blue with cold in winter when water turns to ice, life goes indoors to die after conceiving anew for spring, and so the seasons turn, under heaven. The spirits of the seasons are the Elements, ruling our inner landscape as weather rules the mundane world.

Shiatsu views each living being as a microcosm of the land of the living: elements, meridians, organs, senses, emotions, the physical, mental and spiritual aspects of humanity all interact. Moods, health and wellbeing are ruled by the interplay between the Five Elements. The Elements govern our senses of sight, taste, touch, hearing and smell. Emotions, such as anger, misery, fear, impatience and worry occur through interaction between Elements, and can be soothed or heightened. Positive feelings of kindness, love, calm, courage and gentleness nourish each other and regulate the negative emotions. Each Element is associated with Yin and Yang organ-meridian networks.

Yin and Yang describe the relationship between things, for example men are more yang and women more yin, but among both men and women are those more yin or yang in comparison with others of the same gender. Fire is more yang, water more yin: but as we saw, a candle is more yin than the sun and a wave more yang than a tear drop.

Yin meridians run more on inner aspects of the body and are to do with the deeper organs: heart, lungs, liver, spleen and kidney. The Yang channels flow down the outer aspects and network the more hollow organs: the intestines, bladder and gallbladder. The yin meridians relate to the more inner, emotional and spiritual aspects and the yang to the more physical and mundane. Shiatsu is harmonising yin and yang within Elements, Organs, Meridians and Points.

When Elements nourish each other in the cycle of life:

Sun Fire blesses Earth

Where Metal is born

Metal springs Water

And Water feeds Wood

The Fuel for Fire.

Disturbances can happen, as when too much sun can scorch the earth, so the springs run dry, or too little sun leaves crops unripened.

Elements control one another like a grown-up version of Paper, Stone, Scissors:

Fire melts Metal

Metal cuts Wood

Wood grips Earth

Earth directs Water

Water regulates Fire

In life, full of surprises, metal sometimes refuses to melt, being too strong or the flame too weak; wood can blunt the axe; an eroded earth is too hard or crumbling for roots to grip;   flash floods break the banks; too much fire evaporates water.

In us the elements are so mixed that Nature can stand up and say to all the world, this is a human. It is for the shiatsuka to recognise the predominant element that might be bullying another, or too weak to stand up for itself.

Acting contrary to one's nature can lead to imbalances in the elemental relationships. Take an early riser, a lark, working nightshifts, or an owl who has to get up early. They don't like it. Take an easy-going, happy-go-lucky child born to a driven parent who pressures him or her to "be successful." A recipe for disharmony, which can generate reactions ranging from a vague sense of dissatisfaction to an emotional, mental or even physical imbalance. The Element of our nature is our basic 'constitution.' The distortions result in a 'condition.'

Who do you see when you think of Fire, that warms and comforts, burns and destroys, dances like flame, cannot be grasped?

Who do you feel reminds you of Earth, still, serene, balanced? and hurtling round the sun at thousands of miles an hour.

Can you sniff out a Metal person? bright, hard and sharp, can cut or contain, reflect and inspire. And can be melted and shaped, with warmth.

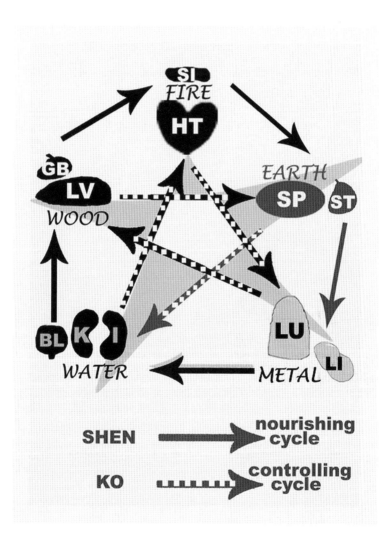

SI
FIRE
HT

GB
LV
WOOD

EARTH
SP ST

BL K I
WATER

LU
LI
METAL

SHEN ──────▶ **nourishing cycle**

KO ▪▪▪▪▪▪▪▪▶ **controlling cycle**

Have you heard of anyone like Water, calm or stormy, destructive or compliant: fits in to anything, can turn to ice or steam, tears or tidal waves?

Do you know someone Wood, with focus and direction, competitive, and grows in all directions?

Each Element has its organ-meridians, each meridian has its points, each point its properties. Understanding these Energy-Spirits is the key to harmonising imbalances. When you follow your hands, you will know where they go, and the properties of where they alight: you combine physical contact with mental knowledge and spiritual power.

Fire

Fire dances, fire warms, fire burns, fire creates and fire destroys.

The sun shines, Fire nourishing Earth, nourished by Wood, controlling Metal, controlled by Water.

Love is the virtue of Fire energy in its positive aspect, while the negative emotion is Impatience.

The Sense of the Fire Element is the sense of Taste, and the feature is the Tongue.

The season of the Fire is Summer, the direction is South and the Guardian Beast the Firebird.

Meridians of the Fire Element are four: Heart, Small Intestine, Triple Heater, Heart Protector/Governor/Constrictor or Pericardium, each of these with a special role in the land of the living.

Heart, a Yin meridian, is the Sovereign, and carries Spirit shining from the eyes. Its sensory organ is the tongue, the communicator. Approach Heart with respect, using the services of its courtiers, the other fire-channels. Heart's body-clock time is between 11 am and 1pm and its seasonal time mid-day.

Close to the centre of the Imperial Court, the Yang meridian Small Intestine is a more playful prospect altogether. Unruly and with a passion for life, the organ-meridian network twists and turns and dances but takes its duties seriously as the court official entrusted with riches and creating change of the physical substance. We might call it the Minister for Recycling, taking the nutrients it needs in the digestive process and letting the waste pass through. Body-clock time follows Heart, 1 pm to 3 pm and seasonal time also mid-day.

Triple Heater, a Yang meridian, represents the three levels of temperature in our being: hot around the head and heart where the fire energy flares, warm around the belly, the home of earth energy, and cool around the kidneys and bladder, source of our water energy. This prosaically mystical meridian has, like the lotus, its head in fire or facing the sun, is rooted in water and, unlike other meridians, has no special organ association (although it could be connected with the diaphragms which unite the upper and lower sections of the torso.) As the body's own irrigation system it distributes energy around the meridian network through the source-points. Body-clock time is 9 to 11 pm and, with the other fire channels, mid-day is the seasonal time.

Heart Protector: a Yin meridian, is Guardian of the Heart and Minister of Fun, takes the first spark of life at the moment of conception, and passes it to Triple Heater for circulation. The physical organ is the pericardium, a thick membrane around the heart itself. This Minister of Fun "who guides subjects in their joys and pleasures" has the cocktail hour as its time, seven to nine pm, and the time where in warm climes young people promenade looking for fun.

Metal

Metal reflects and inspires, cuts and contains, the Element of mystery, of swords and shields, coins, boxes and silver-backed mirrors. Ancient Alchemists sought to transform base metal into gold.

Born in the depths of Earth, Metal nourishes Water. Its sharp edge controls Wood and is itself controlled by Fire as in the blacksmith's forge.

Metal's virtue is Courage and and its negative emotion Sadness with associations of loneliness, isolation and depression.

The Sense of the Metal Element is Smell thus the Nose is the feature of Metal.

The direction is West and the season is Autumn, and the Guardian Beast the White Tiger.

The Yin meridian of Metal is Lung and the Yang is Large Intestine.

Lung supervises jurisdiction and regulation in the land of the living. To breathe in is inspiration, to breathe out is to expire. Lung also governs the skin through which we also breathe, and the hair on the body. Lung's feature is the nose through which the breath of life flows in and out like a tide. Body-clock time is 3 am to 5 am but seasonal time is evening.

Often you will find the body-clock time different from seasonal time. Each meridian two-hour 'period' is high tide for that meridian's energy.

Seasonal time is to do with the meridian's parent Element: Metal as autumn falls in the evening of the day or year followed by Water: night and winter. Wood is in the morning, daily springtime when things begin, Fire in the summer of the day at noon; Earth's time is harvest, late afternoon when work is done and leisure reaped.

Large Intestine, Lung's partner, generates evolution and change, a Minister for the Environment, disposing of waste. Body-clock time is 5 to 7 am and the seasonal time evening, shared with Lung as is the season.

Wood

Spring is in the air! Wood is the Spirit of birth, rebirth and renewal, the unstoppability of Life, the bursting of bud through bough.

Wood energy is dynamic, competitive sometimes to the point of aggression, and powerful. Little plants grow through brick walls and trees uproot pavements.

Wood, tree, plant life, is the element of multidirectional movement: roots penetrate down into the earth, the trunk rises erect towards heaven and branches spread outwards. Trees compete for the light above and shade the earth below. Alive, they are nourished by Water and their roots hold Earth in place. They are cut by Metal and provide fuel for Fire.

Wood takes the conception energy of Water and transforms it into lust for life: survival, sexual desire: continuation of the species, and the need to grow: progress.

126

Kindness is the virtue of Wood energy in its positive aspect, while the negative emotion is Anger.

The Sense is the sense of Sight: ninety percent of our sensory input comes through our eyes.

The direction is the East where things begin and the Guardian Beast is the Dragon.

Wood's Yin meridian is Liver and Yang, Gallbladder.

Liver is competitive, the military General fighting to win. The energy of the Element's season is springtime, of rising sap and urgent juices, the springtime of life that will not be denied. Competitive Liver energy extends into sport with its movement, focus and desire to overcome. Body-clock time is 1 to 3 am and seasonal time is morning.

Gallbladder, an important and upright official who excels through decision and judgment, acts as Executive Officer to Liver and looks after lateral movement. Watch the eyes of someone making a decision! Bodyclock time: 11 pm - 1 am, seasonal time: morning, like its partner-meridian Liver, also of the Wood element..

Earth

Earth is still. Earth is our Mother and provides all our needs. Everything we use comes from the earth and requires only work to transform it into anything from ship to shirt.

Deep in Earth Metal is born. Earth supports Water, is held in place by Wood, and nourished by Fire as the sun shines on the earth giving light and life.

Calmness is the virtue of Earth energy in its positive aspect, while the negative emotion is Worry.

The Sense of the Earth Element is the sense of Touch, and the feature is the Mouth.

The season of the Earth is Harvest-time when the fields are yellow and gold, the direction is the Centre and the Guardian Beast is the Golden Phoenix.

Meridians of the Earth Element are Stomach, Yang, and Spleen, Yin.

Spleen, the Treasurer, has the energy of nurturing resources, caring and sharing, in the nature of the Earth element. Body-clock time is 9 to 11 am and seasonal time, late afternoon

Stomach sees what it wants – the meridian starts at the eyes – and goes for it. This is the meridian of survival, taking you forward to feast your eyes and fill your belly, and is the Official of the granaries and grants the five tastes. Body-clock 7 to 9 am and seasonal time, like Spleen, late afternoon.

Water

Did Life begin when lightning struck the ocean? If Water holds the power of life, it can also carry the power of destruction. It was a

Flood which ended Noah's world.

Water is nature's shape-shifter, freezing solid as ice, boiling to steam, flowing as teardrop or tidal wave. As plain water it adapts to any shape, fits in any container and left to its own devices always flows down to find the lowest level – a good thing to remember when "going with the flow".

Rivers flow into the ocean, evaporate into clouds, rain on the earth and refill rivers. Water nourishes plant life, Wood, and is nourished by the rocks of its sources, Metal. River banks and oceans are held in place by Earth. And Water controls Fire as you know from the barbecue and the Fire Brigade.

Water's virtues are Gentleness and Wisdom, and its emotion Fear.

The Sense of the Water Element is the sense of Hearing: the Ears are the features of Water.

The direction is North and the season is Winter, the time of Death and Conception. The Guardians are Turtle and Deer.

Meridians of the Water Element are Yin: Kidney, and Yang: Bladder.

Kidney: Guardian of ancestral Qi, storehouse of genetic energy, Kidney is "the Official who does energetic work, excelling through ability and cleverness" and thus entrusted with the reproductive essence, the spark passing from generation to generation as the moving qi between the kidneys, captured by the Heart Protector and transmitted to the Triple Heater for circulation, constantly regenerating our life-cycle. Kidney governs the bones, latticed crystalline structures sensitive to the transmission of etheric waves: the first radio sets used crystals. In shamanic traditions of many first-nations changing the bones is a step for transformation. Body-clock 1 pm to 3 pm, seasonal time: night!

Bladder: Bladder runs the length of the back, connecting with the past, routing through nerves along the spine related to the autonomic nervous system that looks after both action and relaxation, storing fluid and regulating vaporisation. Body-clock time 3 – 5 pm, seasonal time: night.

Beyond Elements

Two parental meridians flow outside the elemental structure and, through the energy-centres (similar to yoga chakras) offer direct contact with spirit and connection with the rest of the meridian network.

Governing Vessel, the Yang partner, connects the energy-centres of the back and Conception Vessel, Yin, those of the front.

With my Receiver lying prone I rest my hands, one between their shoulder-blades, behind Heart, and the other on the sacrum, behind Bladder. Thus I start by harmonising the volatile elements of Fire and Water.

Keeping pressure light, await connection and then move one hand up from sacrum to waist, pause long enough to reconnect then move it again, one hands breadth, to beside the one that has been until now the

Motherhand. Slowly disconnect that hand, the one that has till now been still, and move it up to where shoulders meet neck. Pause, connect, then move again, to the base of the skull, the occipital ridge.

Now you must shift the position of your own body, keeping one hand anchored on Receiver, so that you are kneeling or seated at their head. Gentle lifting pressure beneath one shoulder signals them to turn face up.

Connect base of skull, the 'Jade Pillow', to their forehead and then, connected and maintaining the connection, move hand by hand down the front, more or less the same as you moved your hands up the back. Be careful not to apply pressure to the throat itself: rather, place a finger just on the little notch, the supraclavicular fossa, at the top of the breastbone.

End with one hand above and one below the navel centre and complete by bringing their own hands to cover the navel, one atop the other.

I have found this to be a most powerful treatment almost magical in its effect. The spirit-connections of GV and CV with the energy-centres, with the cosmos above and below, seem to unite and harmonise the whole mind-body-spirit being. It is a short treatment, perhaps just ten minutes or so, and the one I would choose if I had only that time available. I also use it to end with when doing longer treatments. Get one for yourself: I did an exchange with a student who rarely used these two meridians as they didn't seem to have any role in Five Elements. Following the treatment she said she would probably specialise in GV and CV.

*   *   *

Chapter 7

Hara Shiatsu:
Deep Diving – the Hara Sea

Hara Shiatsu: Deep Diving – the Hara Sea

Energy blockages arising from organ obstructions and congestion in the abdomen can result in knots and tangles at the centre of the body's vital functions, impeding the flow of Qi, the life-force or bioelectro-magnetic. Emotions such as fear, anger, anxiety, depression and worry are related to different organs. When the Qi of an internal organ is in a state of imbalance, it emanates toxic wind. Diagnosing the energetic condition, the practitioner uses intention and touch to influence the participant's Qi and "chase the winds".

Wind is an energetic vibration, whether toxic or the vital source of life, that enters the being through the "mountains", which include the pointed bones of the nose, coccyx, fingers, toes, knees and elbows. Winds drain out through "marshes" such as the anus, vagina, eye of the penis, pores of the skin, mouth, armpits, backs of knees and front of elbows. The mouth, navel, palm, sole and perineum are among the two-way conduits. A practitioner disperses or directs winds through marsh or mountain, often using supplementary meridians or points.

When obstructed the internal organs store unhealthy energies that can overflow into other systems and manifest as negative emotions and sickness. In search of an outlet these toxic energies create a cycle of negativity and stress, festering in the organs and overflowing into the abdomen, the body's garbage dump. The energetic centre at the navel becomes congested and cut off from the rest of the body.

Where do you feel your emotions? The knot of worry, the slithering eel of fear, the ache of desire, the heat of anger, the butterfly of anxi-ety? They are intensely physical feelings, are they not? In and around your belly. What is happening? Your being is energetically con-vulsed. The Qi, linking mind and body, rushes through the channels like a hot torrent or a sliver of ice, the feeling as quick as thought, energy-intelligence in action. Nerves twist and tighten, cells react, connective tissues writhe, distorting the fasciae of capillaries, veins and arterioles, muscles and organs.

By working in the centre, the practitioner addresses the core of a condition in its deepest hiding place, the junction of the meridians' internal routes; the points of energy infusion; the vortices of the abdominal energy-centres; and the residence of the deities of the internal universe: the major organs in their membranous sacs of protective and connective tissue, attached to and suspended from the spine and edged by ribs, hips, pubis and sternum, and beating with life.

The great arterial aorta runs through, bifurcating at the centre, pumping blood out to the distal parts while a cavernous vein passes the other way lifting used blood back to the heart for recycling, and the vagus nerve runs the communications. A mass of tubes, bladders, reproductive organs pack the spaces, attachments and connections with mesenteric arteries, arterioles, veins and capillaries, lymph nodes

Hara Shiatsu

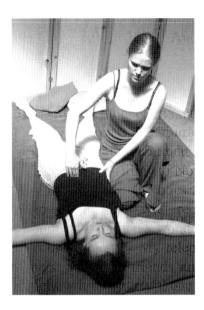

* **Hara** Diagnosis indicates the predominant imbalance among elements at the time of treatment and any resultant changes (post-diagnosis)

* **Bo-point** Diagnosis shows the imbalance between meridians of the element

and nodules, tendrils of nerves, endocrine glands, muscles in broad sheets near the surface and the deep chunky psoas providing a tensile connection between spine and femur. Fatty tissues like rows of sweet-corn and bunches of small grapes cling to the sides of tubes and organs, and the whole and each part down to the smallest cell is protected and connected by webs of fasciae – the connective tissue, from the diaphragm to the perineum, from the centre to the limbs, from the navel to the wrists and ankles. Connective tissue is the common network for bodily systems and energy pathways.

Visualisation by the participant helps the profound effect of this combination of physical, energetic and spiritual therapy.

Focussed massage to points in the navel area slightly melts the gelatinous coating around local cells, releasing suspended toxins into the lymphatic system and enhancing conductivity of the connective tissue, enabling pain-relieving messages to spread through the embryonic meridians radiating out from the navel centre. Knots, tangles and lumps, the aftermath of forgotten emotion, begin to loosen, ready to be unravelled or dissolved.

Toxic winds released are dispersed or directed out through marsh or mountain, combining other, supplementary, points and channels for specific purposes:

Stomach Channel, elimination route from the front points either side of the navel (ST25 in combination with other Front-Mu or Bo points), particularly useful for disturbance of the spirit – emotional – digestive, reproductive, back pain, cardiovascular conditions, stagnation, distortions of the fasciae;

Gall Bladder Channel for the sides, at the point of the 12the rib (GB25) for liver and pancreatic conditions;

Urinary Bladder for the back (UB23 in combination with other Back-

Shu or Yu points) for depletion and kidney conditions; UB51 – particularly effective for tumours and other deep abdominal conditions.

*   *   *

Chapter 8

How to Make a Living Doing What You Love

How to Make a Living Doing What You Love

When I switched from commerce to healing I thought I was doing such a wonderful thing and helping people so much that the world would soon be beating a path to my door. I soon realised I needed to tell them where to find the door. Making my living doing what I loved meant finding enough people to pay me for shiatsu.

How to get the people? I had spent time, money and energy learning shiatsu theory, doing practice-treatments, working in clinics and writing up case-studies. I spent hours at school and hours on private study. Why not invest the same time, money and energy in developing my practice? After years in business and teaching management I knew what to do. Try it for yourself and you will soon be making your living by helping others, doing what you love!

Rules of Thumbs

Treat it like a job. Practice development is too important to be left for when you are in the mood or have nothing else to do.

List everyone you know and tell them that you do shiatsu. Important – you are just letting them know. Leave the rest to them.

Dress the part. Wear special shiatsu-clothes, unmistakeable shiatsu clothes – they don't have to be any particular colour, just what you wear only for shiatsu. It makes you feel special, and your client/receiver/participant feel special.

Be sure to leave your answerphone/voicemail on when you're not available to take calls.

ALWAYS return calls right away.

Spend as̄ much time seeking out new "customers" as you spend on giving treatments.

Your best chance of building your practice is repeat treatments: like a pub, your regulars keep you in business.

Principle of the Zen Bucket: Managing Time

You want to please people, heal them, be there for them, and this is wonderful. You also want to make your living. You want to be available all the time, every moment, to take every opportunity to give treatments, to help others. But what to do when you are not actually in your treatment room? Or visiting clients at home?

Work. Work at building your practice. The key to this is managing your time. Decide what days, and what times in each day, you will do treatments. When Wataru Ohashi set up in New York he allocated just one afternoon a week to giving treatments. He would say "Very sorry, very sorry, I cannot see you for two weeks/months." People would think he was very busy, a successful therapist with a thriving practice. Of course he did not tell people he only saw clients on Wednesdays. Sometimes he would say he could not see them for six months! And then call them back a day or two later saying he had a cancellation for the next Wednesday

Whatever day you decide, don't offer a choice. If someone cannot make the time when you are available, let them go. Apply the principle of the Zen Bucket: Take a bucket, fill it three-quarters full with water. Put your hands in the bucket and try to pull the water towards you. What happens? It flows away from you around the sides. Change your attitude: push the water away…look, it's coming back to you. We all know desire for what is not available.

Soon your Wednesdays will be full. You will be turning them away for two weeks, a month! When you have achieved a three-week waiting list, then open another day, telephone a few people and mention you may have a space for them on, say, a Monday, in two weeks time.

Use other weekdays to build your practice. One effective way to do this is by voluntary work. Yes, work for nothing. Give one day a week.

A Life Worth Living

Mahatma Gandhi said "A life not spent in service is a life not worth living." If each day you can do one thing for the community in which you live, one thing for another person (shiatsu!), and one thing for yourself, then you will enjoy a fulfilled life. And by helping others you make connections that help you.

When I started out to earn my living from Shiatsu, I did volunteer work with recovering addicts in West London. I soon found that many of them enjoyed the shiatsu so much that they booked up for paid private treatments – cheaper than drugs! Non-addictive and satisfying. At their weekly meetings of Narcotics Anonymous, telling their group how they were getting along with recovery since the last meeting, some might mention "and I had a wonderful shiatsu session from Kris who comes to the clinic…" My telephone began to ring with enquiries from others, and their friends and families as word spread through the NA network.

Seek out health-food shops, speak to the manager and offer a free shiatsu treatment, head-neck-shoulders, seated position, absolutely no obligation whatsoever. Offering low-cost shiatsu one lunchtime a week would draw more customers or keep existing ones on the premises longer. Staff will be grateful for free treatments in the quiet times.

If your stool is empty people pass by but if you're working on someone they line up. Don't we always want what someone else is getting? That's the fashion business!

Work on friends and family? Shirley MacLaine wrote that if you want to check out how you're getting on along your new path, spend a weekend with your family! They always see you the way they always did. But as a shiatsu person you are at an advantage – you can offer a treatment. It doesn't hurt and they don't have to take off any clothes. They might turn into clients. They will always remember you. And word spreads!

My own family were scattered across the globe, and I knew few people around where I lived when I started training. But, interested in martial arts and hoping to go to Japan to find the roots of Shiatsu, I joined a karate club and Japanese evening class where I handed out photocopied sheets headlined FREE SHIATSU – SAVE £20! with a few words about the therapy and me as a shiatsu student.

Goodness! The number of people who wanted to save £20 kept me working every night: three nights at classes, four nights giving treatments, shiatsu training at weekends. My confidence grew and I tried calling an ex-business friend – we had socialised around money-making when we worked together before.

"What will it do for me?" he asked. I was ready for this.

"Might help with the headaches."

"How much time? How much money? Does it work?"

"I'm only learning, Simon," I said, "give me 40 minutes and then pay what you think its worth."

"Fair enough."

£20 in the 1980s was a decent amount for my first "paid" treatment. Encouraged, I set out to call around and soon was treating three other ex-business acquaintances and getting well rewarded. I saw them in a new light, these hard-nosed chaps in suits with whom I had wheeled and dealed in the real-estate business, lying like puppies on the shiatsu mat ready for some gentle healing.

Advertising – flippin' AIDA!

Tell the world! Leaflet, flyer, card, brochure, listings, yellow pages, press, internet etc

What you want to say about yourself and what you have to offer? See it from the other person's point of view. Do they know the meaning of those prized new letters after your name? Do they care? Maybe, maybe not, but they do care about the benefits.

What catches your eye in the leaflet racks at the community centre, GP surgery, healthfood shop? Some attract your ATTENTION, others you have to pick out and scrutinise to see what message it is trying to deliver.

Is the message clear? Does it excite your INTEREST?

What are the benefits? Does it appeal to you? Do the words/pictures make you want the product or service? Do they arouse your DESIRE?

And is the next step clear – are you told what ACTION would satisfy this desire?

Make your message yours, and make friends with AIDA. Be clear - about what you want to present. You have seen flyers and ads listing a dozen different therapies offered by a single practitioner, from reiki to soul retrieval via holistic massage and moon dancing. Think of the person reading your words. It helps to take a step back from your self: write what you have to say as if you were writing about someone else, then put your ego in your pocket and ask a friend to read it before you go to print.

Whether business card, leaflet flyer, magazine listing, advertisement or brochure – put AIDA in it.

ATTENTION

INTEREST

DESIRE

ACTION

Carry flyers/cards with you. Look for opportunities to give out: festivals, events, exhibitions....every opportunity that comes up, take it! and watch your practice grow. Don't be choosey – you'd be surprised where you find potential clients/receivers. Exclude no-one.

BE AVAILABLE when people call – after all your creative efforts and distribution legwork – and be ready with your response. Reflect for a moment on your purpose.

Yes, you want to find enough people to pay you to give them treatments. Therefore the people need to make appointments.

Therefore you want them to call you: your immediate purpose is to get the phone-call!

Does this seem self-evident? Agreed, but you can't always be on the end of your phone, so you need a good message. Which of these would YOU like to hear:

"The person you are calling is not available..."

"Sorry I can't take your call right now..."

"Thank you for calling the Shiatsu Practice...."

Get a good message and, if you are serious about being a shiatsu person, say so!

And answer every call right away without delay.

Keeping Clients - the Rule of 3

Oriental Diagnosis is of the relationship between two unique individuals, giver (practitioner) and receiver, as much as of the condition. A close, personal relationship evolves in a shiatsu session. Wataru Ohashi describes how to extend that relationship beyond the treatment-occasion and use it for "client-retention" by applying the Rule of 3.

Contact your receiver 3 days after the treatment-occasion, and ask how they've been and how they are feeling. Spend time talking (that means listening!) to them. Show an interest (be interested!) in their life and the conditions or situations they mentioned at the treatment-occasion. This is not the time to re-book them for another treatment unless they bring up the subject themselves.

Get in touch again after 3 weeks. Find out how they are getting along. Have there been any changes in their condition? Sustain the relationship by taking a genuine interest in whatever is going on in their life. If they mention not having been able to follow recommendations/advice, be supportive rather than judgemental. They are giving you valuable diagnostic information.

Make contact again after 3 months. They will appreciate your interest even if – perhaps especially if – they cannot afford more shiatsu or if life has taken over where they had other plans.

None of your follow-ups are to re-book them for treatments. If they want one they will ask you for it. Let your focus be on fostering the relationship between you, so that they know where and who to come back to in time of need.

Yes, the Rule of 3 means you'll spend a lot of time on the phone. And following the Rule of 3 means you can afford it!

The Popsy Principle – Asking Diagnosis to bring them back

Starting your asking-diagnosis with a little explanation enables you to apply the Popsy Principle. Explain your reasons and seek permission:

"Shiatsu is a holistic treatment, so I'd just like to ask a few things to help me understand you as a whole person...." wait for their agreement "...then we can get on with the treatment and perhaps look at working out some kind of plan that's right for you...."

Start with relatively neutral questions, focussing down the body, asking head-things like job, working down to heart-things like stress, relationships, down to diet, digestive system, down to reproductive issues.

They might ask how many treatments they need. I hesitate to give much of an answer beforehand as I have yet to do the sensing- and touching-diagnoses.

During the treatment ask about pain and sensitivity. Shiatsu styles range from the mechanical to the mystical. A Zen Shiatsuka explores no further than the edge of pain, using it as a diagnostic tool, and is careful to detoxify no more than their Receiver can eliminate.

Afterwards allow your receiver time to return to this dimension. If they ask you what you found explain in everyday language, avoiding shiatsu jargon, and relate the imbalances to what your receiver told you during the asking diagnosis.

Then apply the Popsy Principle, suggesting a course of treatments related to their condition. At least three, perhaps followed by a review of the situation.

When I took my cat to the vet he would always say, "And I want to see Popsy again in two weeks, so please make an appointment with the receptionist as you go out."

He did not sit there anxiously hoping I would want to rebook. He told me to. By doing so, he gave me the reassurance that he was treating Popsy properly.

You have a duty of care to your client/receiver/participants. If you think they'd benefit from more treatments, book them in. Leave it up to them to say no – don't do it for them. Give them the chance and remember – they don't have to be ill to feel better!

Working with the NHS

The climate is changing: it is becoming increasingly possible to get work through Doctors and Hospitals. While the media report news-worthy opposition to new age therapies they do not spare the medical establishment either. The reality is, GPs hear more and more patients asking if they can get any form of complementary therapy on the National Health. There are too many success stories to be ignored even though lacking the scientific research funded by corporate drug barons. I believe fewer patients die from alternative healthcare than from conventional (?!) treatment: and I mean from the treatment, not the illness.

Both have their place: run over by a bus you need an ambulance to Accident & Emergency, not me pressing points. Pressing points might be more appropriate for more chronic conditions. Nowadays as many powerful winds are propelling us towards harmonisation of resources as are trying to blow us away. The Federation for Integrated Health, sponsored by the Prince of Wales, is addressing some of the real worries of the establishment, especially the seeming lack of regulation among complementary practitioners.

Whichever way it goes, there is scope right now for the resourceful practitioner to find work within the system but you will need a little more than skill, understanding and compassion. You need the three Pers: perception, persuasion and persistence.

Perception

Do you see the NHS as illness-orientated, rather than wellness-orientated? Do you see Doctors as overly-busy rather impatient people whose help is restricted to

1) cutting

2) burning

3) poisoning

and Hospitals as places where more die from being there than from the conditions which put them in?

However you see it, the NHS is political: it is something everyone is concerned about, whether their interest is in

a) getting votes,

b) getting cured,

c) getting painkillers.

Because of

a) the system gets tinkered with by whoever is currently trying to get votes so they have the most influence,

b) means most of us at some time come into contact with it,

c) means people can become dependent on it.

Get used to the idea of using the system the way it is. Learn to understand it. To your advantage, the people in the NHS from doctors to administrators know that many patients have experienced complementary medicine and ask about ways (other than the above-mentioned cutting burning and poisoning) of restoring and maintaining health.

Strategic Health Authorities, NHS Trusts, and Primary Care Trusts have the resources to utilise Complementary Medicine. Don't be put off by the jargon and important titles – here's the key that will open the doors – Organisations are run by people

Persuasion

StHAs look after healthcare professionals, PCTs look after the patients, Hospital trusts do both. You might approach an StHA to offer Study-Days to groups of health professionals (Shiatsu and Pain Control? Shiatsu ways to reduce Stress? Effects of Shiatsu treatment on prescriptive-medication Addicts?) Find out who to approach (just ask) and what they need to know to put forward your proposal to their management committee.

At local level, your PCT, its Shared-Partnership associates, and GPs surgeries, approach the Practice Manager, who will want to know what benefits can shiatsu offer.

Help with pain control

Reducing the need/desire for medication

Persistence: Steps through the Doorway

Step 1
To reassure PMs about safety and authenticity, have your paperwork ready – copies of certificates, diplomas etc, insurance documentation, membership of professional association Decide on a scale of fees – don't undervalue yourself but do be willing to negotiate.

Step 2
Find out the name of the Practice Manager at your local GP's practice or PCT.

Step 3
Write them a letter and follow it up with a phone call, or just drop in and make an appointment.

Step 4
Talk a lot. Listen more. Establish a personal connection. Ask if they use other therapies – if not, why not. Ask if they might be open to the possibility that some chronic conditions might benefit from shiatsu.

Offering the Practitioner Manager a free sample/demo treatment gives you a double advantage:

They will be on your side.

They will have experienced what you are offering

Without this, when talking to their principals, the doctors, they will have preconceptions but no real idea of how shiatsu can work for them. You would be negotiating in a vacuum.

Step 5
Explore the practical possibilities of how you could fit in to their system. Agree an outcome, or follow up with a phone call to agree an outcome. Sustain the relationship!

Step 6
Persist.

Step 7
Ask for a referral to their connections in the local hospital trust.

Step 8
Ask for an introduction to their StHA connections if you are interested in giving presentations. StHAs arrange study-days for health-care professionals to learn about complementary medicine because GPs and other professionals do like to appear well-informed.

Step 9
Persist.

Its worth a try. Remember, you are interacting with people who are, like you, interested in healing others....yes, they are - do you imagine your doctor went into the profession to become a stressed-out front for the drugs companies? At the outset, the chances are that she or he had just the same motivation and ideals as you did when you set out to learn shiatsu.

Step 10
Keep trying – Persistence.

Shiatsu at Work

The same principles apply in taking shiatsu into the work-place. Corporate Shiatsu – shiatsu for corporations, who lose hundreds of days a year through staff illness, mainly backpain. You can help.

Step 1 – find the decision-maker in the organisation

Step 2 – find out their needs, show them the benefits

Step 3 – reach agreement for regular visits at a reasonable fee-scale

Step 4 – get it in writing

Step 5 – ask for referrals to other companies

Build yourself a reputation for reliability and compassion, helping the company and its employees gain satisfaction.

Highly creative individuals will know that when they are performing at their best they get into a flow, a state of sustained, relaxed and focussed concentration. (*Emotional Intelligence, by Martin Gorman*)

*   *   *

Chapter 9
Case Studies in the Spirit of Zen Shiatsu

Case Studies in the Spirit of Zen Shiatsu

Case Studies are a remarkable training aid, an excellent way of monitoring one's own powers of observation, and an effective method of a candidate-practitioner demonstrating that they understand the link between skill and knowledge, theory and practice.

A Case Study shows when a candidate has crossed the bridge from advanced student to new practitioner, and attained understanding, as the artist Ryukyu Saito puts it: "When the Zen mind, enlightened and disciplined, is able to rise above mere technique and go straight to the core of being...to reach the soul...the essence."

A Case Study is the story of a treatment, or a series of treatments.

The first two that follow are typical examples of common conditions, Insomnia and Constipation.

Kathy's story (p 163) is unusual in that it is told by the person receiving. The story illustrates how a therapist might explain the complexities of diagnosis to someone with no knowledge of Oriental medicine, a situation met by every shiatsuka.

These three examples are followed on p.165 by helpful notes, guidelines and a possible format for writing a full study tracing a series of treatments, 'Writing a Zen Shiatsu Case Study'.

Treat the format as a memory-aid, to stimulate rather than restrict - a sarong rather than a straitjacket.

A Case of Insomnia

Mrs A, aged 47, had tried different therapies, including western medicine. She arrived with her husband.

In reply to my "Why have you come for Shiatsu?" it was he who responded with, "She can't relax."

She agreed, "I can't relax."

Throughout the asking-diagnosis he answered and she agreed.

She was stiff and nervous. Starting on her side, I found her tension came not so much from stiff joints as a holding-together of herself.

On her back, she flopped, and soon fell asleep. At the end, she was amazed.

"But I can never sleep. I can't relax enough." Husband remained silent.

I said, "Your body has learnt something, even if you didn't think it could."

Treatment had taken effect below the conscious level, where her energy-field, had opened to the possibility of relaxation.

Next time her husband waited outside, and on the third visit she came alone, looking relaxed. She had become able to sleep without tablets, even without reading, and without a light on. Once asleep, she said she now slept through the night.

A Case of Constipation

Reason for wanting Shiatsu:
Ten years constipation, recent headaches. Miss B had tried homeopathy, colonic irrigation, aloe vera and reflexology

Looking Diagnosis:
Facial hue pale, breathing shallow.

Asking Diagnosis:
Busy lifestyle, difficulty letting things go. Diet excluded wheat, dairy, caffeine. Maximum three glasses of wine a day. Regular yoga, walking. Menstruation regular.

Sensing and Touching:
The interplay of elements showed a pattern of swing between over-controlling and neediness in the Ko cycle in the Back (long-term) Diagnosis.

Hara Diagnosis on First Treatment:
Lung/Large Intestine, deficient
Bladder, excess

Treatment Plan:
Tonify the Metal element to improve respiration and excretion.

Tonify Earth element to support Metal in the Shen (Nourishing) Cycle and regulate Water in the Ko (Controlling) Cycle.

Treatment:
First treatment: tonified Lung, dispersed Bladder, tonified Large Intestine 4, Ampuku around Stomach 25.

Post-treatment hara diagnoses showed the same tendency as on the first treatment but a less extreme pattern.

A Case of Constipation (cont'd)

Self-help Recommendations:
Abdominal massage, breathing exercises

Response:
Interesting patterns emerged: when Miss B reported improvement, Hara Diagnosis showed an elemental pattern of neediness. With no improvement or a relapse, Hara showed over-controlling.

Miss B identified stress from life-issues, a tendency to over-control before treatment, and swings between holding and releasing emotion.

Conclusion Miss B was amazed by the improvement over the course of seven fortnightly treatments, felt more in control of her 'healing' and emotional swings, and more connected with her hara. She intended to continue with self-help and return for "maintenance treatments."

Kathy's Story

"My name is Kathy. My health problems – backache, arthritic joints, constipation, frequent headaches, minor ailments such as colds and flu, often feeling under the weather – were typical of what you learn to live with, I used to think.

"Shiatsu had helped others in my family: my daughter's period pains, my son's athletic injuries, my son-in-law with business stress.

"I asked Lee, our Zen Shiatsu therapist: 'Can it cure my kind of problems, or at least help me feel better and cut down the medication?'"

Lee: 'Think of it more as helping relieve symptoms, Kathy. Nature is the true healer, Shiatsu more an intermediary, finding the imbalances, harmonising your energy flow, helping you get in touch with your natural self-healing power. And nowadays, more doctors recommend shiatsu for chronic conditions, so after a few treatments have a chat with your GP.'

"Lee spent time talking with me, finding out about the stress factors in my life, my diet and sleep, as well as enquiring about my various conditions. As her hands gently explored my abdomen, Lee explained the clues she could pick up from observing my features, the hue and texture of my skin, listening to the sound of my voice and feeling the tensions in my body."

Lee: 'For example, Kathy, I can feel your energy is rather low in the meridian network regulating your immune system. This could account for feeling under the weather and being prone to minor ailments. The headaches could be connected with over-activity in another network that might also be related to joint pain. There are other less obvious indications for the chronic backache and constipation.'

Kathy's Story (cont'd)

"Her hands worked, applying light pressure here, deeper there, holding to strengthen where she found energy lacking, soothing and gently stretching to disperse in the over-active meridian. I found myself relaxed, yet felt alert and aware. Almost an hour had passed when Lee stopped.

"I was filled with a most wonderful sense of well-being. My back felt free, my head clear and my joints at ease. I asked Lee about her training. She studied for three years at the Zen School of Shiatsu."

Lee: 'The courses are modular, which suits me as I have a part-time job as well as being a full-time wife and mother. Without other commitments I might have qualified in two years. There is a lot to learn: Zen Shiatsu, Oriental Diagnosis, Taoist Medicine, its underlying philosophy, Western anatomy, physiology and patholo-gy. It's fun, they're nice people and you're treated as an individ-ual. And the student support is excellent.'

"I asked Lee what she thought were the qualities needed to be a Zen Shiatsu practitioner."

Lee: 'I think you need to be a giver. With an open mind, too, because the ideas are so different from what we are used to. And a willingness to keep learning – our main teacher still goes back to his Taoist Master in Asia, to learn like a Beginner again, every time.'

"Lee showed me some simple exercises to share in my own heal-ing process. I felt very satisfied with my treatment and Lee's sym-pathetic approach, and impressed with her professionalism and depth of knowledge. We worked out a treatment plan to suit my particular conditions and circumstances. It did help me feel better, more in control of my own health and less dependent on medica-tion."

Writing a Zen Shiatsu Case Study

Writing a case study is the art of focussed story-telling. Here you show that you understand the ideas behind Zen Shiatsu, that you know how to apply theory to therapy, that you can observe, ask, treat, record and analyse the effect of a series of treatments.

You tell the story of a Participant's progress, elicit patterns, highlight observations and responses to diagnosis, reactions to treatment, and your recommendations for self-help: the healing that happens later when your Receiver has had time to reflect on possible changes they could themselves make to their patterns of unwellness.

As always and in everything, Intuition is your best helper. Insights do come when you sit quietly, without distraction, and meditate upon the person you are about to see for the first time – for even if it is some-one you know well who has volunteered to be your Case-study subject, you will be seeing them with new eyes.

When you begin with some moments of stillness, Mu Shin, open to all possibilities and with no expectations, you may find some insights coming through. You can note these down so that you get them out of your head, in readiness to see your participant without expectation. Then imagine them talking to you. Be open to hearing what they have to say. With your mind's eye look around their energy-field. By the time they arrive for treatment you already have a core of notes but keep these notes random: premature analysis, interpretation or organ-isation can sometimes get in the way of new information. I like to have three corroborations before settling on a diagnosis. For now, trust your instinct.

When it comes to writing up your case-study, see if you can fit it into the following outline. This helps the person reading it to identify areas where you would benefit from feedback and sets a consistent standard.

Format

Between 900 words and 1,100 words. *see below

Write your Name at the top but refer to your Participant only by an Initial.

Describe at least 7 but not more than 9 treatments in each study.

Include a variety of Participants by age, gender, and conditions.

You have a limited number of words, so:

*   FIRST – write down everything that comes in to your head

*   SECOND – take your scalpel and edit, edit, edit

    SLICE AWAY – repetitive phrases, long-winded descriptions, listings of superfluous elements, lists of things that aren't symptoms, waffle and verbosity eating up your word-credit

*   THIRD – show your case-study to a friend – they don't have to be a shiatsu-person – and ask them what words they would cut

*   FOURTH – final surgery

Case Study Guidelines

First Impression

What is your instinct telling you?

What is the first thing that strikes you about your participant?

What do you see as their build, movement, complexion, voice, most prominent feature, obvious imbalances?

Why have they come for treatment?

Medical History

Specific conditions, operations, injuries, treatments, current medication, other therapies, family medical history/tendencies?

Personal

Gender, age, occupation

Relationships: with partners, children, parents, siblings, colleagues

Lifestyle, exercise, relaxation/recreation, habits, addictions

Sleeping pattern, diet, digestion, prescriptive or recreational drug use

Menstruation, general energy, sexual energy

Outlook on life. What makes them happy/upsets them

Self-perception – how does he/she see her/him-self?

Diagnosis

What is the 'personal environment' that has allowed conditions to take root, develop and flourish?

What seems to be the energy-pattern?

Why? – explain your reasoning.

Compare with first impression? This is the core section.

Case Study Guidelines (cont'd)

Treatment Plan

What are your Treatment Aims based on your Diagnosis?

How do you plan to achieve those aims?

Treatments Given (List as 1 to 7, 8 or 9)

Date	*Kyo*	*Jitsu*	*Energy-Pattern*
Yu-pt	___	___	_____
Hara	___	___	_____
Bo-pt	___	___	_____

The Treatment

Meridians treated: tonified/sedated?

Points treated and why?

Hara post-diagnosis:	___	___	_____
Bo-pt: changes?	___	___	_____

Recommendations/suggestions: exercise, diet, meditation, lifestyle, self-perception

Reactions to previous treatment/recommendations/suggestions ?

[NOTE: **Hara** Diagnosis indicates the predominant imbalance among elements at the time of treatment and any resultant changes (post-diagnosis). **Bo-point** diagnosis shows the imbalance between meridians of the element.

Energy Patterns show the state of ongoing change: trends linking Asking/Looking and Sensing/Touching, common factors, insights into the core issue leading to possibilities of restoring harmony: by treatment, recommendation, or both.]

Case Study Guidelines (cont'd)

Treatment Analysis – What is the Story?

What are the main issues? E.g. 'Earth imbalance, indicated by an abnormally yellowish hue and a craving for sweets... (distinguish between 'abnormal' signs of imbalance, these being indicators of the element of your participant's current CONDITION, and the 'normal' indicators of their CONSTITUTION or naturally pre-dominant element).

Were the presenting symptoms directly or indirectly related to the main issues?

If not where did they come from?

Did the condition change during the period of treatment? To what?

Were there any discrepancies in the patterns? Any reason you can think of?

Comment only on those elements involved in the primary imbal-ance (and a secondary one if significant) rather than all the elements.

Is there a predominant energy pattern?

Does the final analysis correspond to your original diagnoses?

Was the original treatment plan followed? If not, what was it that took the treatment series in a different direction?

What trend do the Energy Patterns indicate?

Is there something left over that the Participant may have to address or which may appear in subsequent treatments?

Case Study Guidelines (cont'd)

Conclusions

How did the Participant respond to the treatment process overall?

Did they follow recommendations?

Would you make any further recommendations?

How do you see the self-healing process developing?

Chapter 10
Coping with Assessment

Coping with Assessment

The prospect of putting myself in front a panel of assessors woke me up to a sight of myself I had avoided. Leaving school at fifteen innocent of qualification, up through the ranks of Her Majesty's army omitting 'education' in the promotion forms, sailing through Teacher Training College with an hour's revision and three memorised quotations from Maslow and Rogers, I had, at fifty years of age, completed three years shiatsu training and was ready for final assessment. I spent time choosing that word ready. I did not feel ready. My shaking hands and liquid guts were sending frantic "we're not ready" signals. Brain was trying to escape.

Study had been hard for me: most of my fellow-students had left school around ten years before starting shiatsu, many had been to university, all knew the habit of studying. The system then was to accumulate knowledge before putting it into practice. They would take notes at lectures while a teacher wrote meridian theory with squeaky chalk on a blackboard.

Hundreds of treatments had built my confidence on the practical side: I had developed a practice in West London from the out-clinic work. Clients, all members of N.A., promoted me at their weekly meetings, said Shiatsu was cheaper than coke and left them feeling just as good.

Three months before Final Assessment – see how the capital letters jump into place! – I gave in to panic, stopped practice and withdrew into my narrowboat on the Regents Canal in Little Venice. I had the advantage at the time of not needing to earn money, having saved enough from wheeling and dealing in the property market.

I had begun to take notes in what was to have been my final term but then walked out when that school's owner and main teacher decided to add an extra and then unnecessary year to the curriculum. I could see no reason for this other than to benefit from extra fees. And the leaky umbrella organisation of the old governing body – of which he was an office-holder – went along with it in those days before the independent General Shiatsu Council. I knew I would be facing that teacher on the Assessment Panel. Did I have any chance at all of getting through?

Three months full-time studying, all day every day and most nights. My mind felt like a sieve – was this the same for everyone? Friends came to my boat. We revised together. They all knew much, much more than I. Not only had they taken notes, they had "written up" those notes. What was this mysterious process, writing notes about notes?

I had flashbacks to classes at school, problems such as how many men does it take to mow a five-acre meadow if each man mows fifty square yards: I could only think of going out and finding a meadow, men and mowers. And if x equals y what is z? A letter of the alphabet, of course. I was accustomed to getting around 2% for maths exams although I did once reach 40%. I felt like an alien.

Looking back, I cannot believe the sustained concentration. I was trying to learn everything and, in Anatomy and Physiology, knew not where to stop. There was little guidance and no guidelines. We had no Assignment system such as at the Zen School where each module specifies what you need to know for both intermediate and advanced assessment. With hardly a cohesive reading-list I bought shiatsu books, Chinese medicine books, macrobiotic books, wrote out lists of meridians, lists of points, lists of conditions, lists of lists.

Somewhere along the line a light glowed when I realised that if asked about a condition there were just two main things to consider: which part of the body it was in, so what was the local meridian, and which organ-meridian network governed that condition, e.g. Kidney for bone-conditions, Liver for ligaments etc. Understanding could do a lot when memorisation faltered.

Still, some things I could make neither head nor tail of, such as the lists of conditions related to an extended meridian system, a protocol thought up by a shiatsu-practising psychologist based on his own clinical practice. Here I could find no logic-alternative to memory. Not very Zen, I thought, but then maybe the nature of Zen is in imperfection.

I overstudied. I got fed up and tired. I began to think of how I could make my living at shiatsu without taking any exams. Had I not been doing so before stopping to study? I wouldn't want to work in a clinic, I wouldn't need insurance, I wouldn't need membership of any professional body, I wouldn't need a shiatsu teaching certificate: I already held Cert.Ed., a nationally recognised proper qualification. There! I wouldn't need to take an assessment!

I would give up. I always had. I would turn away from the challenge. I would reinforce my pattern and collude with my conditioning.

"What's the big deal?" said Emma, a study-mate visiting my boat. "What's the worst that can happen?"

"I fail," I said.

"And you've never failed? Not at anything?"

"Well, yes. But I do tend to avoid it."

"So you don't even try? Is that what you call succeeding?"

"Why does it have to be either?"

"It doesn't. It's just a matter of completing, of doing what you set out to do. Now you're faced with completion you're hiding in your Zen refuge, using it as an excuse. Chill out, calm down, and have a go. At least you'll learn what you don't know instead of living in this constant panic-state."

Thanks, Emma, I thought and took many deep breaths as I went into the room of serious people in white, a few carrying clipboards, others looking sick and nervous. I ran out to the toilet, let go, more deep breaths and then back in. And then it was a blur of faces and questions and answers until I faced my former teacher. I felt OK then.

I had faced my fear. I had broken my pattern. I felt alive.

I thought of my mum.

One month after passing I dropped everything, picked up my backpack and set off around the world. My plan was to learn more, by meeting remarkable men and women, to fulfil childhood dreams: trek the Himalayas, walk the Grand Canyon, see the Declaration of Independence, and new dreams of finding spirit.

*   *   *

Training Information

Students in search of the right path, whether shiatsu, life or any other are, perhaps by definition, impressed by teachers, by seniority and, in the case of shiatsu or similar oriental-medicine-based therapy, by orientalism. Ohashi attributed much of his early success in New York – perhaps the least gullible city populace – to his oriental appearance, Japanese accent and broken English avowing, moreover, that he turned such apparent disadvantages into marketing opportunities.

You will find the right teacher for you. You may have already. Let Spirit guide you, and follow your instincts. Everything is learning, everything is perfect.

When you find your way to the Zen School, you start with a warm welcome and complete with a proper qualification.

Zen School Training comes in three stages: Basic, Intermediate and Advanced.

Basic Learning

Learn the Ropes – start anytime! Learn how to move around, how to give a great shiatsu treatment, to protect yourself from needless back-pain, or energy depletion and contamination; to develop sensitivity; learn what conditions are best left alone until you have more experience, and which ones are contra-indicated anyway.

Learn the art of gentle healing. Learn something about yourself, too, and of the gift Nature has given you for this work.

Intermediate

The Theory behind the Therapy

Get to grips with the ideas behind the movements, in a Journey through the Philosophy of Yin and Yang, the Five Elements, the

Fourteen Meridians or Energy- Pathways and their access points (tsu-bos).

Study and practice Oriental Diagnosis in harmony with Western Anatomy, Physiology and Pathology: the best of apprentice-style learning combined with state of the art cross-modular educational techniques.

Prepare an Assignment, attend a Tutorial, Practical Application, and Learning-Treatments in your own time. Do the homework, discuss theory with your Tutor and other students, apply it under supervision, then reinforce it by learning-treatments on family, friends and, for informed feedback: fellow-students.

Advanced Learning

How to make your living doing what you love

Putting it all together: Apply your learning to field-work: help out at clinics; voluntary work-placement; demonstrations at festivals, exhi-bitions, corporate events and community activities; gain priceless experience of the human condition in all its wonder and variety - develop your heart connection, put your compassion into practice.

Weekend Study-Days offer fresh angles and insights into theory and practice, while case-study tutorials, Supervised Practices and repeat-ing Basic and Intermediate Modules refresh your earlier learning.

By the end of this course you let go of the intellectual mind-set and follow your hands. Your knowledge and experience, with our train-ing and help, gives you confidence to set up and run your own prac-tice.

You have begun to build a base of client-friends and enjoy a gift of life: to make your living doing what you love.

*   *   *

Contact Information

You will find full information on the Zen School of Shiatsu web site, www.learn-shiatsu.co.uk, or call +44 (0) 20 7739 9916 for a printed prospectus, or write to

Zen School of Shiatsu
1st Floor
68 Great Eastern Street
London EC2A 3 JT

or email info@learn-shiatsu.co.uk

Web site: www.learn-shiatsu.co.uk

International Contacts

Australia
Shiatsu Therapy Association of Australia
PO Box 91 West Brunswick, Victoria 3055
enquiries@staa.org.au www.staa.org.au

Canada
Kokoro Do Jo
358 Dupont St. Toronto. Ontario, M5R 1V9 Canada
kokorodojo@mac.com www.kokorodojo.com

Europe
Shiatsu International
Maulak Chambers The Centre High Street Halstead CO9 2AJ UK
admin@shiatsu-international.com www.shiatsu-international.com

New Zealand
Metta Shiatsu
23 Champion Terrace, Tahunanui, Nelson
shiatsu@wildhealth.co.nz www.mettashiatsu.com

South Africa
Association of Creative Thought
PO Box 5301 Walmer Port Elizabeth South Africa 6065
actpe@intekom.co.za   www.intekom.com/actpe/shiatsu

United Kingdom
Zen Shiatsu Society
1/68 Great Eastern Street London EC2A 3JT
society@learn-shiatsu.co.uk   www.zen-shiatsu-society.co.uk

United States of America
Boulder College of Massage Therapy
Boulder Colorado 80301
info@bcmt.org   www.bcmt.org

*   *   *

Glossary

A&E – accident and emergency department
Ampuku – shiatsu style
AV – anti-vehicle mine
Bhagavad Gita – Hindu holy book
Brahma – Hindu god
Brahmin – Hindu priest
Chakra – energy centre
Ch'an – meditation
Chillum – hashish pipe
Chi Nei Tsang – hara shiatsu
Dan – grade, degree
Dakhini – tantric nymph
Dhyan – meditation
Ghat – place
Gai-Jin – foreigner
Gi – uniform
Ginza – district of Tokyo
Gurkhas – Nepal martial tribes
Halal – Muslim protocol
Han – Imperial dynatsy
Hara – abdomen
Janet Reger – exotic underwear
Jitsu – excess
Kahuna – Hawaiian shaman
Kalashnikov – automatic rifle
Kali – Hindu goddess
Kamba – tribe in Africa
Kannon – Kuan Yin, Goddess of Compassion
Ki – energy, power, life-force
Ko – controlling

Koan – riddle

Krishna – Hindu god

Kyo – deficient

Lathi – wooden staff

Leela – the comedy of life

Malla – prayer-beads

Masai – tribe in Africa

Masunaga – shiatsu style

Mu-Shin – clear mind

Namaste – palm-press greeting

Namikoshi – shiatsu style

NLP – neuro-linguistic programming

Ohashiatsu – shiatsu style

PCT – Primary Care Trust

PM – Practice Manager

Puja – prayer

Qi – energy, power, life-force

QiGong – exercises to stimulate energy

Saddhu – Hindu holy man

Satori – ultimate clarity

Shen – spirit, nourishing

Shiatsuka – shiatsu therapist

Shiva – Hindu god

StHA – Strategic Health Authority

Tikka – "caste" mark

Tsubo – acu-point

Vipassana – Buddhist insight meditation

Wadi – desert valley

Wei – Imperial dynasty

Zazen – seated meditation

Zen – meditation

*   *   *

Bibliography

Bandler & Grinder
The Structure of Magic
Science and Behavior Books 1975
ISBN: 0-831-40044-7

Beinfield & Korngold
Between Heaven & Earth
Ballantine Books, New York U.S.A, 1991
Random House, Toronto Canada, 1991
ISBN: 0-345-37974-8

Beresford-Cooke
Shiatsu Theory and Practice
Churchill Livingstone, London UK, 1996
ISBN: 0-443-04941-6

Chia
Chi Nei Tsang
Universal Tao Publications
ISBN: 1-594-77105-7

Deshimaru
Questions to a Zen Master
Arkana 1985
ISBN: 0-140-19342-1

Foreign Press Beijing
Chinese Acupuncture & Moxibustion
Foreign Language Press, Beijing China, 1980
ISBN: 1-405-2-90350-0

Gurdjieff
Meetings with Remarkable Men
Penguin 1991
ISBN: 0-140-19037-6

Hix
14 Classical Meridians
Rosewell Publications, Peterborough UK, 1998
ISBN: 0-953-3850-0-0

Jarratt
Nourishing Destiny: the Inner Tradition of Chinese Medicine
Spirit Path Press, Massachusetts U.S.A, 1998
ISBN: 0-966-9916-0-5

Krishnamurti
Meeting Life
HarperSanFrancisco 1991
ISBN: 0-062-5-0526-2

Lao Tsu, tr Gia-Fu Feng, Jane English
Tao Te Ching
Vintage; 25th Anniv edition 1997
ISBN: 0-679-77619-2

Matsumoto & Birch
Hara Diagnosis: Reflections on the Sea
Paradigm Publications, Massachusetts U.S.A, 1988
ISBN: 0-912111-13-5

Ouspensky
In Search of the Miraculous
Harvest/HBJ 2001
ISBN: 0-156-00746-0

Sergel
The Macrobiotic Way of Zen Shiatsu
Japan Publications 1989
ISBN 0-870-40671-X

Veith
Yellow Emperor's Classic of `Internal Medicine
University of California Press 2002
ISBN: 0-520-22936-3

Author

Master of the Zen School Kris Deva North integrates the principles of ancient healing traditions with modern Life-training techniques from the Mind Dynamics of the 1970s to state-of-the-art Neuro-Linguistic Programming.

He founded the Zen School of Shiatsu in 1992 after a lifetime of travelling, learning from Masters in Japan, Thailand and USA; living with Kali-worshippers of Nepal; travelling with a Buddhist monk; learning with Shiva Saddhus in the Himalaya, Shamans of Africa, North America and Hawaii, and Aboriginal men of high degree in Australia.

Kris has been involved in healing meditation since 1972 and Taoist practice for over 20 years.

He has appeared on UK national TV, demonstrating Taoist Healing and Tantric practices, in programmes such as Emma Freud's series on Bliss, Nick Hancock's Sex and Stopping, Carlton TV City Survival Guide, and was consulted for the Sex Inspectors.

In 2004 Channel 4 made an observational documentary on his work teaching the Taoist practices to a group of celebrities on an uninhabited island in the Andaman Sea.

Kris has written numerous articles on shiatsu, tantra and meditation and co-authored with Mantak Chia the book 'A Touch of Sex: Shiatsu Secrets for Love', Universal Tao Publications, November 2005; and with Catherine Rowan 'The Story of Su Nu', September 2006.

*   *   *

AFTERWORD

I did learn more, and I did find spirit: following my knows it would jump out from unlikely places and slap me. I found the world quite small, and that love does make it round. I found my school which has turned into a love-lee community of like-minded people and found, too, the meaning of enlightenment:

"Enlightenment means – lighten up!" TOM ROBBINS

Thank you for reading!

LET GOOD FORTUNE JUMP ON YOU

A Touch of Sex: Shiatsu Secrets for Love

by Mantak Chia & Kris Deva North

"Well presented book. As a chinese massage and herbal practitioner specialising in working with reproductive and sexual issues, it is always good to see material like this. Suprising too, as my experience of the Shiatsu world (many years ago) was that there was no understanding of the importance and power of sexual energy for healing and that the whole subject of sensual touch was totally taboo!" Nicholas Hudis.

Master of the Zen School Kris Deva North and the Taoist Master Mantak Chia combine their years of teaching and depth of knowledge and experience to create a compelling journey through the secret 'erotic pressure points' of Chinese Medicine.

'A Touch of Sex: Shiatsu Secrets for Love' reveals the secrets of Taoist Foreplay, from its origins at the Court of the legendary Yellow Emperor through 4,000 years of sexual history to its relevance for modern lovers: combining loving touch with healing power.

"Sexual practices have been studied for centuries in both East and West," says Chia." Chinese and Japanese traditions combined the study of sex with medicine: certain pressure-points and meridians were found to stimulate and sustain sexual desire. Using the secrets of these points and channels makes for longer and more pleasurable sexual encounters. Peak moments can be prolonged beyond bliss, into ecstasy. Like cooking a Chinese meal, preparation is the key."

"Yes, you can become a far more effective Lover," adds North. "Woman, man, straight, gay and bi, you can please your partner and please yourself. The act itself is natural. You know what to do. It is the moments leading up to the act which make it more or less pleasurable for your partner. Women fear insensitivity. Men fear inability to perform. Both fear rejection. Knowing the psycho-sensual secrets of certain pressure points helps you become a better lover, however good you are already.

"Are you aroused more quickly, your partner more slowly? Its quite usual for the man to climax first. Woman comes to the boil more slowly but simmers longer. He's done in, she ready for more."

Based on the form of a conventional shiatsu treatment, the text and pictures give detailed guidance, showing precisely where to place the hands - and other body-parts - to stimulate and sustain arousal.

Many of the pressure points from shiatsu healing massage are shown with their more arcane applications, sometimes with passing reference to the clinical use, for example:

"Conception Vessel 1, known as the Gate of Life and Death, so named because the retention of sexual energy is said to prolong life, has subtle use as arousal point for both sexes, especially good for prolonging male orgasm. Clinical use is said to be able help with prevention and relief of symptoms of some prostate conditions."

Self-shiatsu is well covered, with exercises for men and women to keep themselves at the peak of sexual fitness, and the women's practice of using the famous Chinese Drilled Jade Egg is described in detail.

A chapter on what to look for in a lover, from astrological compatibility to physical attributes as indicators of sexual performance, is followed by advice on coping with sex-vampires and energy-parasites.

It is Mantak Chia's twentyfirst book, and the first by Kris Deva North. The book shows a profound knowledge of the subject, which it conveys with a light touch and hundreds of colour photographs.

For this and other Universal Tao Publications including the complete range by Mantak Chia please visit our web site:

www.healing-tao.co.uk